GU00985735

METHUEN YOUNG DRAMA is a series w
new plays for young people. Different vol
for different age groups, drawn from the e
created by a number of modern playwrigh
theatre groups and theatre-in-education cc
by an account of the original conception a
are given for future presentation.

'The MYD format is neat, tough and cheap, a good fit, in both senses,
for the pocket of a pair of jeans.' John Coleby in *Drama*.

SWEETIE PIE was devised by the Bolton Octagon Theatre-in-Education
Company to explore and demonstrate the gulf between the myth and the
reality of a modern woman's expectations. Centring on the life of Margaret
- alias Sweetie Pie - fresh out of school and ready for a fairy-tale romance
and a happy-ever-after marriage, the play offers a series of episodes from
her real life - getting married, setting up house, coping with children,
making ends meet, getting a job herself, becoming pregnant again and
trying for an abortion - and counterpoints these ironically with an
idealized version retailed to her by Mr Cash, her ever present confidant
and evil genius.
Specifically created for performance with the minimum of resources,
Sweetie Pie has succeeded in provoking and entertaining teenage and
adult audiences alike. In her Introduction, Eileen Murphy, formerly a
member of the Company, gives an illuminating account of the work of
the group on this play and others.

RECREATIONS
two plays by John Challen
**(Pilgrim 70; Transformation
Scene)**
for 11-14 year-olds

PLAYSPACE
four plays for children by
contemporary writers
(The Cutting of Marchan Wood
by Richard M Hughes;
The Boy without a Head
by Edward Lucie-Smith;
Tamburlane the Mad Hen
by Adrian Mitchell;
**The Legend of Scarface and
Blue Water**
by Niki Marvin)
for 8-14 year-olds

**JOHN FORD'S CUBAN
MISSILE CRISIS**
a play put together
collectively by the
Bradford Art College
Theatre Group
edited and introduced
by Albert Hunt
for 15 year-olds upwards

**THE ADVENTURES OF
GERVASE BECKET**
or The Man Who Changed
Places
a play by Peter Terson
originally written for the
Victoria Theatre,
Stoke-on-Trent
edited and introduced by
Peter Cheeseman
for 8-14 year-olds

SNAP OUT OF IT
a programme about mental
illness
devised by the Leeds
Playhouse Theatre-in-
Education Team
edited by Roger Chapman
and Brian Wilks
for 15 year-olds upwards

TIMESNEEZE
a play by David Campton
originally written for the
Young Vic Theatre Company
for 7-11 year-olds

OLD KING COLE
a play by Ken Campbell
originally written for the
Victoria Theatre,
Stoke-on-Trent
for 8-12 year-olds

SCHOOL FOR CLOWNS
a play by F. K. Waechter
translated by Ken Campbell
first staged by the Unicorn
Theatre
for 7-12 year-olds and upwards

THE INCREDIBLE VANISHING!!
a play by Denise Coffey
originally written for the
Young Vic, London
for 8-12 year-olds

RARE EARTH
a programme about pollution
devised by the Belgrade
Coventry Theatre-in-
Education Team
for 9-11 year-olds

PONGO PLAYS 1-6
Six plays by Henry Livings
with music by Alex Glasgow
for 12 year-olds upwards

SWEETIE PIE

A Play about women in Society

Devised by the Bolton Octagon
Theatre-in-Education Company
With an Introduction by
Eileen Murphy

First published in Great Britain 1975
by Eyre Methuen Ltd
11 New Fetter Lane, London EC4P 4EE
Reprinted 1978
Introduction © Eileen Murphy
Sweetie Pie © 1975 Bolton Octagon Theatre-in-Education Company

ISBN 0 413 33670 0 (Paperback)

CAUTION

Printed in Great Britain by
Whitstable Litho Ltd., Whitstable, Kent

Introduction

The Octagon Theatre, Bolton, opened in November 1967; an exciting building with fully flexible stage area. The Theatre-in-Education department, which began work at the same time, was conceived as an integral part of what was intended to be a lively community theatre. For the first year the team of actor/teachers did peripatetic drama teaching in schools and colleges. It was when Cora Williams (a member of the first Theatre-in-Education group at the Belgrade Theatre, Coventry) came to work in the department, that the theatre-in-education method began to be developed in Bolton. Five years later it is a measure of the team's success that there is scarcely a school-child in the town who, seeing the team's yellow van approaching, doesn't hope 'the Octagon's coming to us today'. Four years ago, when the Local Education Authority cut part of their contribution to the team's grant, the local headteachers guaranteed sufficient from their capitation allowance to keep the department open.

What is the Theatre-in-Education Method?

It is not actors from the local rep going into schools to dramatise passages from examination texts and advertise their current production. It isn't commercial children's theatre or drama teaching, though it can include some techniques from both. It is a group of actors, in character, and a group of children (or young people or adults) exploring and living through a situation in which they are physically and emotionally involved.

It can include scripted dialogue between actors, but most of the 'script' is improvised by the actors and by the individuals with whom they are working, and results directly from their reactions to the situation which has been created. The programmes can have a set ending or be open-ended depending upon the subject matter and the age of the people for whom they are devised. The actors are both a focus of attention and a stimulus for the children's involvement, and they use their combined talents to encourage the children to express and work out their involvement as individuals and as part of a group. The children don't pay anything for a visit from most Theatre-in-Education Companies; such companies are financed by the Arts Council or the Local Education Authority, or both.

As an experimental method theatre-in-education can, and does, fail. When it succeeds, however, it creates real moments of theatre and drama and provides a vivid first-hand experience. This is sufficient end in itself but can also prompt exciting follow-up work.

What are Actor/Teachers?

A cynical student once asked whether actor/teachers aren't, in fact, drop-outs from teaching or the theatre. Apparently he hadn't considered that the most talented members of both professions can be driven by impossible conditions to drop out and pool their talents in an exciting new method of working. The term 'actor/teacher' has provoked much query and argument; it isn't necessary here to fix a precise definition of the job, but members of a successful theatre-in-education team must be excellent performers with a firm interest in and knowledge of children. In the past, actor/teachers have, for the most part, been actors wanting to work with young people, or teachers who also have strong performing skills, but there is no reason why these two professions should be the only recruiting ground. Most theatre-in-education companies devise their own material. It is, therefore, essential that the members of a team can contribute ideas for new programmes, as well as having the ability to research and devise them and the imagination to know what will involve the children.

As a performer in schools the actor/teacher has to hold an audience which has neither the desire nor, sometimes, the sophistication to conceal boredom; and he has to do it in surroundings which, far from having any of the technical advantages of a theatre building, frequently include a rich variety of unpredicted distractions. I think with satisfaction of the time a description of my life in Mexico-Tenochtitlan not only won the attention of forty eleven-year-olds against the challenge of a loud hammer in the same hall, but eventually persuaded even the hammerer to stop work and listen. I am less smug about the time the school caretaker, thoughtfully tiptoeing so as not to disturb us, got stuck in the doorway with a long ladder and stole at least that part of the show.

Teaching experience is a great help in devising material and methods of presentation for different age groups. Most theatre-in-education programmes are made up of sessions of activity and discussion within the context of the story. During these sessions a class works with one or more actor/teachers; the actors must supply necessary information, draw out ideas, help to develop them, and try to make sure that each child is involved. To do this he uses many of the skills used by teachers, but he is always in character; his teaching and discipline depend entirely on his ability to interest the children in himself, the other characters, and the problems and challenges of their situation. So performing and teaching are used in varying degrees at different times; obviously not all members of a group possess these skills equally, but one of the great strengths of this method is that the team members support and complement each other.

A genuine interest in working with children and young people is an essential qualification for an actor/teacher. The greater part of children's theatre has suffered from writers who are not excited by their audience: they write plays for children because it is an easy market, the directors knowing and caring as little about children's tastes as the authors. One director, frustrated by his audiences' record number of trips to the lavatory during a particularly boring children's show, later remarked, 'The trouble with children is they don't know a good play when they see one'. The conditions of employment in most of the travelling children's theatre groups are so bad that most actors work in them just to get their union card: they leave before they have had a chance to appreciate the potential of their audience or demand better material to perform. Companies like the Octagon Theatre-in-Education team, with comparatively good conditions (including long-term contracts) and serving a fairly small geographical area, can get to know their audience, develop exciting and challenging programmes, and, in turn, attract good people to work with them.

What makes a good T.I.E. programme?

Before looking specifically at *Sweetie Pie* I will say a little about the work of the group as it had developed up to the writing of the play. It will necessarily be a brief and selective description, not a comprehensive study, but I hope it will give some idea of the way the team's experience in Bolton schools affects the development of the work; and of how the successes and failures of each programme not only provide part of the challenge of the next, but add to a tradition of experience which is constantly referred to and reassessed.

Poverty Knocks, for instance, was a history programme in three parts for top junior and lower secondary pupils. The first and third parts were visits by the Company, and the second part was project work done by the class with their teacher. The aim of the programme was that the children should become aware of the conditions of the working class in Bolton in the 1830's by experiencing them, and that they should participate in the Chartist activity in the town, which grew out of the need to improve these conditions. It would, of course, have been impossible, and undesirable, to make the children experience the filth, near starvation and exhaustion in which most people lived in those days, but we were able to create a programme in which they could be browbeaten, cheated and humiliated, and in which they would experience anger, determination and solidarity.

The characters in the programme aren't intended, as in the traditional theatre situation, to be the main focus, to involve the audience mainly through identification. They are used to delineate situations which force an immediate physical, intellectual and emotional involvement onto the children, who are the main focus for most of the time. There is, nonetheless, a very strong identity with certain characters, not because that character is experiencing for them but because they are going through the same threats and problems together. The children don't act: they are themselves within assumed group roles, such as hand-loom weavers, or factory workers. They wear their ordinary clothes, as in all our programmes, although the actors wear full nineteenth century costume.

Eleanor and the two-thirds of the class who are factory workers go through the harsh discipline of the factory (the classroom); the overseer, Denton, fines individuals for supposed misbehaviour and, on the least pretext, cuts their meagre wages and puts them on short-time working. They are particularly indignant when a round-robin they have all signed as a protest petition is torn up in their faces. The fun the children get out of tricking Denton and surreptitiously collecting signatures is an element which should never be precluded from a theatre-in-education programme.

The hand-loom weavers, working with a middle-aged woman, Hannah, at home in Croal Court, may at first be a bit in awe of her grief over the death of her young son, John. His coffin is still in her house (Croal Court is an arrangement of gym mats around a prop pump in the hall). However, as they learn about their housing conditions, as they feel anger and humiliation when the price for their cloth is cut once again, they see her trouble as part of their own, arising directly from the appalling conditions in which they live and work.

When both groups of workers meet and discuss what has happened to them, Denton, the overseer, is spoken of with bitterness and fear, as the man who, while cheating the hand-loom weavers out of a fair price for their cloth, deducts a comparatively large sum for the rent of the damp, decaying cellars in which they live. The vicar is another character against whom the Croal Court community unites – he extorts four shillings from Hannah for performing the funeral service for her son, despite explanations that she only has five shillings to last the week.

Before the end of Part I of the programme the children see a notice: 'A Commissioner is coming from London to inquire into sanitary conditions; prepare your reports'. They agree that they will put all their grievances into these reports; surely the official from London will instigate reforms.

The project work done with the teachers in Part II – about Bolton in the 1830's – varied in length and content according to the teacher's assessment of the class. There was some very exciting work done; the range varied enormously but it all started from the same basis: the inhabitants of Croal Court, humiliated by Denton and the vicar, were eagerly discovering more about the objective conditions which caused their poverty and were preparing written, visual or verbal reports to explain the injustice of their case. The personal experience of Part I gave them a strong motivation for their project work, which was almost always written in the first person.

Part III, the second visit from the Company, begins with the visit of the London Commissioner. The class and Eleanor, excitedly clutching their reports, wait for the great man to arrive. The urgency of the situation is increased when Eleanor tells them that, because she had absolutely no money left, Hannah has had to go into the workhouse. The Commissioner arrives, sniffs the Bolton air and, true to historical fact, beats a hasty retreat, covering his nose with a scented handkerchief and completely ignoring the children and their reports. They are frustrated, indignant and angry — it is weeks of hard work spurned. The Commissioner has put them firmly in their place, where they have no privileges or rights. The energy generated by this disappointment, the experience of Part I and the work done in Part II mean that the children are ripe for the introduction of Chartism by another character, Jack Broadbent. Although he explains the principles of Chartism very simply, some children find them rather difficult to understand; but this does not matter because they are all quite clear about their grievances and understand that, by joining forces, they can attempt to change their conditions. So, when they make banners for a protest march round Bolton, at the height of their involvement in the Chartist cause, some banners carry the official slogans of Chartism: GIVE US THE VOTE, LET US VOTE IN SECRET, while others give immediate expression to local grievances:

GET RID OF DENTON

FAIR PAY FOR OUR CLOTH

WE DON'T SMELL, YOU DO

We found that *Poverty Knocks* had the qualities essential for a successful programme — good material presented in such a way that the children had an essential part to play, and interesting characters who could bring a lot of pressure to bear on them. It doesn't need to be an obvious, positive, pressure — some of our most useful characters have had limitations for which the children have had to compensate. Willie, in an infant programme, broke his leg; while he sat apart, gloomily watching the activity of the market, individual children would leave their work there to come and stare at his plaster and offer sympathy or compare ailments. Mr Homer was a blind man in an adventure programme for older children; they guided him, told him what was happening and protected him when he was vulnerable. But to avoid easy sympathy for people with handicaps, some of our characters have been needy and nasty. Tom was dumb; the children did help him but they would get furious when he stole things from them. In the same programme a bad-tempered old woman, dirty and shabbily dressed, would pester individual children for money to feed her cat. When they refused she would shout at them and say they were cruel to animals (this accusation always provoked indignant enumeration of well-fed dogs, cats and tortoises); significantly, when they had to decide whether or not to throw her out of the caravan in which she had squatted, the great majority of classes chose to evict her.

It is a common fallacy that junior children will participate whole-heartedly and secondary children won't: that for them it must be straight theatre. Their involvement may come more slowly — there is often suspicion among older pupils who haven't worked with us before — but the group has learned to prepare for this initial reticence. The lead into the programme can be more gradual. For example, *John Chamberlain* was a programme for fifth and sixth formers about work in a car factory. We announced ourselves as the Octagon Theatre-in-Education Company and asked the class to choose a certain number of quality controllers and managers from among themselves (a choice which was particularly interesting in view of the conflict and friction which often followed). The rest of the group were workers; they started to make cardboard cars, cutting, painting and assembling them. If they had chosen to do so, they could have sat at their workbenches all morning. But gradually things would begin to happen: complaints about blunt tools, work coming in too slowly from the previous stage, election of shop stewards to go to negotiate wage increases with the Management, Union meetings, more work sessions. During this activity the conflicting personalities of the characters representing either Management or Workers would become known. At the time this programme was running the Industrial Relations Bill was being debated and eventually came into force as an Act. It was a turbulent time for industrial relations, and the latest news would be used in the programme every day. It was open-ended. A class which became very militant might side with Jean Dukes, the character who was a member of a revolutionary group, in which case the programme sometimes ended with the occupation of the factory. A more conservative class would probably side with the A.U.E.W. convenor, who believed in co-operation with the Management and might put up no fight when Dukes and other militants were sacked. It was almost always a very exciting session.

We are convinced also of the potential success of the theatre-in-education method with children who have special needs. We did a three-part programme for junior immigrant children. It wasn't intended to be a language course, but a stimulus for their use of English, and it worked very well. On another occasion we did an adventure pro-gramme for less able secondary children, again with good results.

However, the group doesn't limit itself to the theatre-in-education method. We recognise the strength of straight theatre and have used it in both junior and secondary programmes, when we thought it was better suited to our material.

Do They Believe It?

Very often observers and new members of the Company are concerned that the involvement of younger children will diminish if they no longer believe that the events and characters are real. The children never seem to worry. (Their playtime and classroom selves are probably a much more complex mixture of reality and play than adults remember.) If the actors are true to their characters then, for the children, that is who they are. As actors often stay in the Octagon department for a long time, they inevitably work with the same children more than once, but multiplicity of personality doesn't seem to cause confusion. In one school we were doing *The Promise*, the immigrant programme, which a very distinctive-looking member of the Company, who wasn't in the programme, had come to observe. At one point a ten-year-old boy came over to him and said, 'Excuse me, are you from Mexico-Tenochtitlan?' Clive said, 'Yes', and the boy, quite satisfied that it was indeed Captain Cortes, carried on with his activity in the current programme.

Historical costume, of course, is a clear indication that the events are a story, but adventure programmes, which are contemporary, are more difficult, because anyone in the school or street could be an Octagon actor and have some relation to the plot. A kindly vicar was rather disturbed on one occasion when he asked a group of ten-year-olds, working in his churchyard, what they were doing today. He was met by cold stares and sealed lips — he had intruded on their investigation and might even be a spy. In the same session a quite genuine old woman sitting on a park bench was nearly rushed when someone suggested that she was probably the baddy in a wig. Even quite young children who know the programme isn't true have a complex view of its relation to reality. In their discussion during *Spy Ring* a class of seven-year-olds had decided by a majority vote that the scruffy, nasty old woman should be thrown out on the streets. As they saw her shuffling down the road, homeless, some of them began to regret their decision and a tremendous argument followed. In the classroom shortly afterwards one boy, who couldn't stand the weight of guilt any longer, announced, 'Well, it doesn't matter — it was only the Octagon'. He was vehemently attacked from all sides: 'Well it's the same as if it was real' . . . 'It's just like you, that is!' . . . 'We'd have done the same if it was real, wouldn't we?'

Any adequate study of this question would be very long, but I think it is worth mentioning two occasions on which the balance between play and reality was tipped in favour of reality. The first was the programme for less able twelve and thirteen-year-olds. We built an elaborate set in our own studio, and the classes came to us. But because we were not in their school and because we never said it was a story, some children went away thinking that the adventure really had happened. It was in many ways an excellent programme, but in retrospect we thought that the omission was a serious mistake. We mustn't con the children into a state of confusion but have confidence that they can work on two levels, that they can enter fully into a situation while being quite clear in the back of their minds that it is not true. The second occasion was when we did some *Spy Ring* shows in Rochdale, using our distinctive-looking van for the caravan. The van was always immediately recognised in Bolton, so that when the characters drove off in it at the end, children knew that they would probably meet them in some personality or other again. In this sense the show was part of a tradition of working in the Bolton schools, which the children knew would continue. But in Rochdale no-one recognised the van, they thought the situation was quite real. Learning from our former mistake, we had asked the teachers to tell the children, after we had left, that it was a story; but when we drove off, we felt that they were overwhelmed by the experience and by the finality of our departure. There appears to be a safety level of belief about our work in Bolton which is desirable.

'Drama Is For Thickies'

Bolton Borough Council, under the Tories, has constantly resisted the establishment of comprehensive secondary schools. The schools aren't called Grammars, Secondary Moderns and Tecnhicals; they are often built on the same site, and many people in the Authority claim that the system is an ideal combination of the old grammars and the comprehensives. There is an eleven-plus exam taken by all the children in the top junior class, although, again the name has been changed. There are also five direct grant schools in the Borough. The teachers' opinions about the merits of the system vary, but few would deny that the curriculum is geared to the passing of examinations. I don't intend to discuss the system in detail here, merely to point out some of the ways in which it affects the work of the Theatre-in-Education Company.* On one occasion, when we were doing *Poverty Knocks* with a top junior form, the head-master confided that he was glad he had booked us for that particular day because the class had just got their eleven-plus results — we were a reward for those who had passed and a consolation prize for those who hadn't. We expressed disagreement with a system which labelled the majority of children 'failures' at the age of eleven. The headteacher assured us that, not only had the children known who was going to pass, but they had known from the age of seven! He had never given them or their parents any false hope on the report cards they had taken home from the first year in his school.

There are obvious contradictions between such a system and the kind of work done by a Theatre-in-Education group like the Octagon's. Some are shown clearly in the number of bookings received for different pro-grammes. There are always too many bookings for an infant or junior programme, because the work fits well into the project methods used in

*My remarks throughout apply to the Borough as it was before the 1974 local government re-organisation.

most primary schools, but secondary schools book badly — their time-tables are usually divided into 40 minute periods and a theatre-in-education programme usually lasts between one and a half and three hours. We expect the teacher who has booked the programme to be present throughout — she usually has an integral part to play in follow-up work — but that means a complex re-arrangement of the timetable; other teachers understandably resent losing their free periods; some regard the programmes as superfluous, since they bear no direct reference to the examination syllabus. Our work rarely fits into any one subject slot — it can be relevant to the teaching of History, English, Humanities, General Studies. There are some excellent teachers in both primary and secondary schools who use our work very imaginatively and provide valuable criticism and suggestions. In primary schools different specialists often co-operate over the project work, but this rarely happens in the secondary schools. Despite constant denials on our part, there is still the attitude, 'If it's the Octagon, it's up to the drama teacher' — and Bolton has very few drama specialists.

So, frequently, secondary programmes do not 'pay for themselves'. A great deal of research and rehearsal time is spent on them, and few bookings are made. It is in secondary schools that we most often feel that our aims and methods are completely at odds with the rigidly-streamed, exam-orientated system. Drama teachers both inside and outside Bolton find some of the same problems: they have a slot in the timetable, 'as long as they don't make a noise', but the difference between a drama lesson and most others is so marked that it is often either chaotic or deadly dull. Other teachers mistrust the subject, not just because the method of teaching is different but because less academic children are often good at it; they don't consider that the method could be used in different contexts to discover talents that more traditional methods have missed. They view it as one of those subjects, like cookery and needle-work, which are useful insofar as they fill up the timetable of those not academically gifted: the 'drama for thickies' view.

We had an excellent session one day with a top junior class and spoke enthusiastically about the children to various members of staff afterwards; but rather than showing interest that the 'B' stream had been inventive, quick to grasp the situation, and both sensitive and vigorous, they all assured us that the 'A' class would be much better the day after. Nothing went wrong the following day, but nothing 'sparked'; the level of involvement was fairly superficial. We were disappointed, of course, that it hadn't been a very good show but felt a good deal of satisfaction that the streaming system had been proved unjust. The class teacher didn't see it that way: 'Well, we do find that drama goes down well with the less able'.

This attitude isn't unjust only to the children in the lower streams but also, in a different way, to those who are considered too bright to benefit from new teaching methods. Children who are constantly competing academically at school and encouraged to this end at home often develop a wariness of any method of working which doesn't include a text book. Used to succeeding at school where the rules are made with them in mind, they are insecure and cautious when involved in a different teaching situation, afraid to fail or be laughed at. Children who have failed already, who are not in the top stream, commit themselves much more quickly; they haven't mastered the rules of academic success, so they don't depend on them for security: they accept new methods of working with relief and eagerness. Although of course there are many exceptions, we frequently find that the most creative theatre-in-education work is done by children in the lower streams. This distinction becomes very marked if we compare 'the best' and 'the worst' schools in Bolton, i.e. those with the highest number of eleven-plus passes and those with the least. They are divided on class lines. The top nine schools get between 76% and 100% passes: they include four fee-paying prep schools and five schools in middle-class areas, where parents are very anxious for their children to do well, they know exactly what is required and are able to provide a great deal of help. The bottom nine schools, which achieve between 3% and 15% passes, are in working-class areas. Often a high proportion of the parents are subsisting on low wages or social security. They are just as concerned about their children's education but are unable to provide the help required because they are failures themselves, and their mistrust of school and teachers makes co-operation very difficult. It isn't possible to present this case in sufficient detail here, but it must be said that there are numerous written reports in the Theatre-in-Education files describing shows in middle-class schools which went smoothly but produced little originality; on the other hand, shows in Educational Priority Areas are sometimes said to have 'gone over the top' or to have been too long for the children's span of concentration. They are always very hard work, but they almost invariably include some exciting and original contributions from the children and a very high level of involvement.

I have gone into such detail about the school system in Bolton not only because it raises problems which the team has to cope with every day, but because it was the only common political experience of the group before the writing of *Sweetie Pie*. I don't wish to belittle the good work which is going on in Bolton schools, but it is going on despite the system rather than because of it; nor do I underestimate the generous co-operation of many of the teachers who have worked with us — our work wouldn't have succeeded and developed as it has without their help. But, working in most schools in the town, from the poorest to the most affluent, we are in a privileged position to judge the system and the assumptions on which it is based. Those assumptions are in direct contradiction to our working experience with the children and to the aims of the technique which we have painstakingly developed over a period of six years. At the time we came to write *Sweetie Pie* the political opinions and levels of political activity in the group were diverse, but we were in complete agreement about the education system.

SWEETIE PIE

When we start to prepare a new programme, one actor is usually time-tabled to begin exploring possible subjects and methods of presentation, and he is joined at a later stage by other members of the group. In the summer of 1972 we began work on a programme for sixth formers by looking for subjects of current interest which might make a good pro-gramme. The whole Company met to discuss the suggested topics and the man doing the preliminary research put forward Women's Liberation as the most likely; it proved to be an explosive suggestion. I was an active member of the women's movement and, although I was aware of the propagandist value of such a programme, I felt that we shouldn't do it. Far from being committed to the movement, there was a great deal of unquestioned chauvinism in the group; our motives in choosing the subject at this stage were tainted by the spurious topicality created by condescending press coverage, and I resented the fact that hard work done by small women's groups should provide easy material for a theatre group riddled with chauvinism.

As an actor/teacher I valued the integrity of the team. I thought we should continue to devise programmes in which we believed; the other members of the group agreed but felt that, once the matter of male chauvinism had been raised, it had to be thrashed out. There were several sessions of argument, emotional, painful and confused, but in many ways positive. Eventually it was decided that we should do a programme which was consciously biased in favour of women's liberation and which bore reference to the four demands put forward during the national demon-stration the year before:

1) Equal educational opportunity.
2) Equal pay.
3) 24-hour nurseries.
4) Free contraception and abortion on demand.

It is easy to simplify the effects of those arguments; I couldn't attempt to write an accurate account of what they meant to each individual. But it is important to say that each actor/teacher, including myself, changed in some way, did reassess both his position within the group and his general opinions; it is important because we were all involved in the writing of the play. Actors frequently do work they don't like and don't believe in, but *writing* a play you don't believe in is more difficult – especially if the process of writing is a shared one. The problems that we worked out in that early research period were bound to arise during improvisations; without agreement we would have become cynical and hopelessly divided. The upheaval in the group was part of the creative process insofar as it prompted a degree of self-analysis and a strong commitment to the play and to the political line it was to embody. In turn this commitment informed the performances and carried those parts of the script we feel are weak. Audiences recognised that the actors really wanted to communicate with them, a rare experience in much of today's theatre.

Research

We researched the programme on many levels — we read Greer, Millett and Firestone; and many of the pamphlets and periodicals published by women's groups were a great help. At the same time we were relating these general sources to specific work we were doing in Bolton: in one exercise we went out onto the street and made lists of the different activities in which men and women were engaged, and of numerous signs of discrimination; things which hadn't been noteworthy before suddenly came into sharp focus — women with children and heavy bags, many more men driving cars, male supervisors over all-female shop staff, and separate windows for job advertisements in the employment exchange (the women's rates of pay being little over half those of the men). Advertisements were a study in themselves — from the most obviously sexist, in which female nudes were used as part of the soft sell, to the cliché and sentiment surrounding homes, husbands and children . . . 'Behind every great man, there is a woman who builds him'.

We saw strict role division catered for on shop counters from the pink and blue baby clothes, the Action Men and ironing boards in the toy shop, to the chemist departments — Eyelure and Femfresh for the ladies and Old Spice for manly men. We saw tired, heavily pregnant women gazing forlornly at the absurd and elegant Mothercare models and we remembered the Bolton junior school in which the children still obediently divide to follow the 'Boys' and 'Girls' signs down the corridors. We looked with increased awareness at the press: Oliver Reed had been giving yet another interview in which he expressed his offensive and asinine opinions of women. A dull morning was transformed when we discovered the sexist Marjorie Proops article which we eventually used in the script. In the Octagon itself, the lowest paid workers were the cleaning 'women' and the coffee bar 'ladies', and there was a dispute in progress backstage: could a woman take over the stage manager's job? The presumption finally used to dismiss an extremely suitable candidate was that 'she couldn't handle the A.S.M.s'.

A great deal of material came from the group itself. Unlike a history programme or a show like *John Chamberlain*, in which most material came from outside research, we found with *Sweetie Pie* that, once we had begun to look for signs of sexual conditioning and discrimination, we reviewed our own experiences in that light and found lots of suitable material in the process. The three women in the team, especially, wanted to make a great many points: small signs of condescension which had rankled for years were now fitted into the complex pattern of discrimination.

Theatre or Theatre-In-Education?

We amassed a great deal of material. We first thought we would use it in a theatre-in-education programme, even though we realised that we would be faced from the beginning by the derided image of women's liberation created by the media. It would have to be a long programme; we wanted the sixth formers to trace the process which the group had gone through, to begin to realise how many of their own opinions and reactions were based on role indoctrination; but we also wanted them to realise that role division plays a crucial part in the maintenance of the status quo. We felt we would need a whole day with one class. It seemed most unlikely that many schools would be prepared to give us so long: the number of bookings, always low for secondary work, would be unrealistically small.

Theatre seemed to offer some advantages. By using a variety of theatrical styles to present our material, we could show that the typical image to which women try to conform, far from being just, is ludicrous and potentially tragic. Much of the material we wished to use — marriage, the loneliness of being a housewife — was outside the experience of most sixth formers. We didn't merely have to create a character with whom they could identify, through whose experience they could see the gaps between image and reality — much of the reality we had to show was destructive to the stubborn myths on which they were building their own hopes and ambitions. The advantages of a strong script in such circumstances were obvious, and we chose to do a straight performance — it was the first full-length script that we had written as a group.

Writing the Play

In preparing a theatre-in-education programme, we improvise to explore situations and develop character; only a few of the sessions are rehearsed into a final form and scripted. We used the same method to write *Sweetie Pie*, but, as we wanted a finished script, we were trying to find a shape for the play as a whole. The women's movement had postulated four demands — we wanted to show the women and the situations which made the demands necessary. We felt that shouting slogans wouldn't be adequate. The popular reputation of the movement was such that we would have been met with scorn and laughter. We would be much more effective if we presented characters whose problems made the audience sympathetic, angry, and, perhaps in a minority of cases, committed.

We decided to show the life of one woman. We had written a short scene about women's liberation in a previous programme *Blood, Sweat and Tears*; in that scene the woman had been middle-class, with a good job and a husband who worked at home and was prepared to help with cooking and cleaning. The three middle-class women involved in the writing of *Sweetie Pie* certainly wouldn't deny that the character had difficulties, but this time we wanted to show the humdrum problems resulting from shortage of money and lack of nursery facilities. We wanted a very ordinary woman so that the audience couldn't say that her difficulties arose because she was unusual. So she must be a working-class woman, and almost inevitably, because of the group's strong identification with the town, a woman from Bolton. We presented her life over a period of ten years in order to show the difference between her expectations and her real life; we hoped that the sixth formers would identify with someone of their own age and that their awareness of the naiveté of her first ambitions would grow along with hers.

Improvisation

To those theatre people, and there are still too many of them, who regard all improvisation as indulgent rubbish, our work will undoubtedly seem experimental and risky; but to those who are interested in developing improvisation as a valuable technique, our methods probably appear conservative. They have the strength of having worked time and again and, with the pressures of a very full schedule, we continue to use them; nonetheless we frequently wish we had the time to try a greater variety of approaches.

In writing *Sweetie Pie* it was an important advantage that the group had worked together for some time. We had experienced all standards of improvisation, some horribly bad, some excellent, so there was no feeling of competition, of trying to prove oneself better than the others, as there often is with actors working together for the first time; we knew each other's capabilities and could listen carefully, pick up lines and develop them. If a particular improvisation was bad, we would admit it had failed, try it in a different way or scrap the idea altogether. We would set up the situation in some detail, it might be a telling incident that we had seen, or a theoretical point which we wanted to express theatrically. A good first improvisation might give us a single line that we thought worth keeping, an effective move or, frequently, a powerful emotion, clumsily expressed; we often taped sessions and would go back over the recording to find promising bits and develop them into a rough script. This, in turn, would be tried and altered further, or eventually discarded. So, for example, in the scene where Margaret takes off her blouse, to seduce Bob, the one line which sounded absolutely right after the first improvisation, was his initial response 'the kettle's boiling'. His preoccupation, amazement and complete lack of sexual interest was neatly expressed in one practical comment — we changed the rest of the scene several times but we worked around that line, and it became the comic watershed for the dreariness and humour of the entire scene.

The improvisations for the scene in which Margaret and Carol discuss pregnancy came to life when we started to use the second-hand baby clothes: these were an important second best as it was impossible to use real children in the play, but they are such an important part of many women's lives. The activity of sorting and lending the clothes is typical of the practical preparations for childbirth, almost invariably accompanied by reminiscences, terrible, practical and superstitious: 'Look at me, my third took the longest and I had to have ten stitches. Eh, there must be two cords. Well, I hope it's the lad who comes out first, 'cos they say "First out is the most intelligent" '.

The period of improvisation was by no means always exciting; but because of the ubiquitous nature of the subject, we continued to find new material which renewed our energies and enthusiasm. We were in contact with the local Women's Liberation Group and went along to the council meeting when their proposal for a free family planning service, already passed by the Health Committee, came up for debate. We cut and rearranged bits so that it needed only three actors, but we added nothing and the final tenor of the speeches of Councillors Cash and Broughton are not exaggerated above the original. (Those who suspect that Bolton councillors are unusually straight-laced are advised to read the Hansard of the parliamentary debate on the same topic which took place a year later. Local chauvinism is faithfully reproduced at national level.)

The scene about the rent rise was another one which was almost ready-written for us. The rent strikes against the Tories' Housing Finance Act began in October 1972. It was largely a women's struggle, and the failure of male trade unionists to realise that 'a rent rise is a wage cut' is one of the reasons it didn't succeed. It caused bitter division in many council homes, not just over payment of the £1 increase, but because, despite their husbands' opposition, women were suddenly organising, leafleting and picketing. For many of these women it was the first time they had made an independent stand and tested their political strength; we wanted to show Margaret take just such a step before her unwanted pregnancy threatened to destroy the limited independence she had gained by working.

Language

Since our production of *Sweetie Pie* I have seen another one in which the clichés used by Carol and Margaret have been spoken so as to deride the characters. I wouldn't deny that many of them are humorous, but one of the discoveries we made in writing the play — and one of the aspects of women's problems we wanted to highlight — is that such clichés are the only language which women have to describe certain areas of their experience such as childbirth. They are composed from several largely alien vocabularies:

The medical: cervix, contractions, placenta.
The religious: fruit of the womb, flesh of my flesh.
The commercial: 'those special months and the comfort of Lucozade'.

There are no words in widespread use with which women can describe sex, pregnancy, and childbirth as they, individuals, experience them. They must think of themselves as consumers, trying to fit into the Mothercare image, or as the embodiment of the sanctity of womanhood, or as a medical case. This lack of vocabulary (and it exists for all women in different degrees, middle-class as well as working-class) puts Margaret at a crucial disadvantage when she is trying to explain her case for an abortion. The gynaecologist uses a wide range of expressions, from the coldly medical: 'Did you have regular periods before conception?' to the most sanctimonious and sentimental: 'Now pull yourself together for what to other women is a happy event'. Margaret is condemned as a 'healthy female' and as a 'selfish woman'. She can only say: 'But I don't want the baby'. This is a powerful argument to those who believe that women have a right to control their bodies — but it carries no weight at all with most doctors and law-makers. The problem is clearly expressed by Sheila Rowbotham in *Women's Consciousness — Man's World*:

The underground language of people who have no power to define and determine themselves in the world develops its own density and precision. It enables them to sniff the wind, sense the atmosphere, defend themselves in a hostile terrain. But it restricts them by affirming their own dependence upon the words of the powerful. It reflects their inability to break out of the imposed reality through to a reality they can define and control for themselves.

The fact that Margaret couldn't express herself adequately was, of course, a problem for us in writing the play, and a related difficulty arose when we came to present certain parts of our material: for example, in the housework scene we wanted to put a new slant on activities which are very common background material; there was a danger that the scene would be too typical to be meaningful and would bore the audience, especially as the 'new slant' was to show boredom and isolation as a serious condition. To some extent society has admitted that there is a problem and has proceeded to exploit and belittle it in the sale of pills and tonics — these transform the tired and irritated mum back to her all-comforting real self. Little is known about the long-term effects of the conditions in which ordinary housewives try to make sense of their role in society, but the facts that are known — that one woman out of six spends some time in a mental hospital, that doctors are prescribing an increasing number of strong, anti-depressant drugs for housewives —

are never correlated in an analysis which might shake the belief that a woman's place is in the home. So Bob thinks that all Margaret needs is a bottle of wine to cheer her up; Mr Cash tries to dissuade her from going out to work, but she is determined. Even though the combination of low wages and high nursery fees means that it is impossssible for her to go at this stage, she has, for the first time, expressed her doubts about the ideology which conspires to keep her at home.

Mr Cash

Theatrically Mr Cash is the chief foil to Margaret's lack of articulation. He presents the ideal for her to match. Her failure to do so, and her eventual questioning of the ideal, are effective largely in contrast to his verbosity. We wrote most of Cash's script without improvising, though with frequent reference to the Bible, fairy stories, women's magazines and party-political broadcasts on behalf of the Tory party: without such constant reference our attempts at satire paled in comparison with the originals. He introduces and controls the evening, and has complete mastery over the language — he uses it to persuade, patronise, indoctrinate and frighten Margaret. Other characters are frequently his mouthpiece: for instance, in the comic role-learning of the 'ideal wives' scene — 'We wash, we sew, we iron, we mend. We arrange, we dust, we polish, we tend' — and the more subtle instances when the conservative propaganda seems to come from Margaret herself: 'You're just the same as all the rest — sheep following them commies'. Cash fosters and uses Bob's sexist attitudes to the same end: 'You had no right to sign that petition. If I say we are going to pay the increase, we'll pay it'.

Margaret's rebellion at the end, the immediate result of having failed to get an abortion, takes the form of rejecting Cash's pet name for her. We first thought of, and improvised, a long declamatory speech, but we knew it wasn't right — she wasn't the kind of person who could or would make such a speech. Her awareness of Cash's control over her life is still incomplete, but her refusal to accept that her pregnancy is for the best and her insistence on her real name are significant challenges to Cash. They don't destroy him — we are not yet at that stage — he is ruffled and discomfited, but still in control.

Abortion

This is the most controversial and crucial of the four original demands. The group decided to show full support for the right of women to have control over their bodies and to choose when to have children, both by the use of contraceptives, easily and freely available, and through abortion on demand. In the booking form for *Sweetie Pie* we gave details of the content of the show, and we were never booked by a Catholic school (several individual Catholics, who saw the show as part of a general audience, enjoyed it very much, though they could not agree with the end). Our reading about women who had both succeeded and failed to get abortions showed that the patronising attitude of the G.P. in the play and the viciousness of the gynaecologist are very common. The British Pregnancy Advisory Service was one of the few organisations in the country to give a counselling service rather than a moralistic refusal or such grudging consent that the woman feels guilty.

The change in Bob's attitude to the abortion is one of the most optimistic developments of the play. From complete condemnation at the beginning, he comes to realise that it must be Margaret's choice — it will be her life which will be most radically altered if she has the baby. He comes to support her in her struggle and to resent the pressures which eventually defeat her. We wanted to show a new potential in the relationship between Margaret and Bob which could be developed despite, or in opposition to, Mr Cash.

We didn't decide for a long time whether Margaret should get the abortion or not, we didn't want the audience to say, like Cash, 'You'll be as pleased as I am when the happy day arrives', feeling that she would have regretted it if she had had the abortion. So initially we worked on an improvisation in which she succeeded and did not regret it. On the other hand the facts are that many women, especially working class women, fail to get the abortions they want; the prejudice of doctors, the delays of long waiting lists and the cost of profit-making clinics frequently defeat them. Two women writers, watching a session in which we were trying to resolve the end, said they preferred the second alternative: it was more typical of the way things were. We finally decided to accept their suggestion because, theatrically, it worked better too; instead of Margaret's challenge to Cash coming from partial triumph, it comes from utter depression. We hoped that this inane cheerfulness would be in contrast, not only to Margaret's despair but to the hostility of the audience, and this was the way it worked. His last speech was often delivered into an ominous silence.

The complex process of devising this last part of the script became much more difficult when in the Autumn of 1972 — the middle of the writing period — we appointed a new actor/teacher. He was a Catholic and irreconcilable disagreements about the question of abortion held up improvisations for some time. The majority of the Company were unwilling to compromise on the line we had decided. Eventually the Catholic actor decided that he would not take part in the last sequence of the play (later in the run the appointment of another actor made it possible for him to leave the show altogether). In many ways it was not a satisfactory compromise; if he had been a member of the Company at the beginning of the research period, I doubt that *Sweetie Pie* would have been written at all. With the play already booked, we took a majority decision which inevitably caused great tension in a very small team and seriously alienated one member during his first working period with the Company.

The days immediately before the first performance were hectic; we survived them, and, after that performance, our mood was triumphant. We felt it was a good show, but, as actors, we knew we would have benefited from a little time in which, untroubled by unfinished bits of script and belated practical and technical arrangements, we could have concentrated exclusively on our parts and coped with the strains peculiar to a first performance.

At the end of each performance we distributed handouts which included a number of sexist quotations from our research as well as details of the Merseyside Pregnancy Advisory Service and of the local Family Planning Association and Women's Liberation Groups.

Eileen Murphy

Characters

MARGARET - 'Sweetie Pie'

MR CASH (Still obviously CASH, he also portrays:
  Vicar
  Radio Announcer
  A Councillor
  T.V. Compere
  G.P.
  Gynaecologist)

BOB, Margaret's husband

ARNOLD SMITH ⎫
DINKIE DOLLERY ⎬ All three suitors can be played by one actor (possibly the actor who plays Bob)
ZOOT SIMS ⎭

ANITA
FASHION EDITOR
MRS KING, Margaret's mother
JOAN
MISS FORSYTHE
CAROL, a neighbour ⎫
WOMAN ON RADIO (Auntie Sally) ⎬ In the original performances all these characters were played by one actress
MARJORIE PROOPS ⎭
NURSERY WOMAN
ANGELA, Margaret's sister
COUNCILLOR BROUGHTON
FLORRIE
SAMANTHA
RECEPTIONIST

MR KING, Margaret's father
FASHION EDITOR'S ASSISTANT
POSTMAN
MILKMAN ⎫
ENCYCLOPAEDIA SALESMAN ⎬ In the original performances all these characters were played by one actor
CLERK ⎭
COUNCILLOR WILLIAMS
WORKMAN
MR CROSS

Sweetie Pie was devised by the Bolton Octagon Theatre-in-Education Company between June and October 1972 and first presented in Bolton in November 1972, remaining in the repertoire until July 1973. During all or part of this period the members of the Company were Ron Blenkinship, Linda Broughton, Neil Coldwells, Jonathan Cross, Terry Enright, Jim Hooper, Mick Jones, Mike Kay, Eileen Murphy, Malcolm Padmore, Marjorie Richardson, Clive Russell, Dave Swapp and Cora Williams.

Enter CASH.

CASH: Good evening. My name is Mr Cash, and today I would like to read you a story from my book. This book was compiled by many men with a deep insight into man's spiritual, cultural and commercial aspirations. It has a foreword by an archbishop, a signed picture of the Queen, and many articles by leading statesmen and dignitaries. It is, of course, available at all branches of Cash's book shops, priced five pounds ninety-nine pence, and makes an excellent gift for any special occasion. Today I'd like you to meet one of my most admiring customers. A young lady to whom I have been reading these stories since — well, since she was this high. Her real name is Margaret, but I always call her Sweetie Pie. Ladies and Gentlemen — Sweetie Pie.

MARGARET (entering): Hello, Mr Cash.

(CASH kisses her on the forehead.)

CASH: Come and sit down, Sweetie. Today I'm going to tell you another story . . .

MARGARET: Oh, is it about . . . ?

CASH: Ah! Ah! No peeping, Sweetie. But I will tell you: romance is in the air. Ready? Off we go.

(MARGARET listens, entranced.)

CASH: 'Once upon a time, not so very far from here, there lived the prettiest Princess you've ever seen. Her real name was Margaret, but to all who knew and loved her she was affectionately known as — Sweetie Pie.
'Now, one morning, Sweetie Pie awoke bright and early and decided to go down to the lily pond to pick a flower for cook, who had promised her a freshly-baked jam tart if she came round to the kitchen later that day. So, skipping lightly across the palace lawns, she sat down small and neat by the lily pond. Then, as she stretched out her hand towards the prettiest lily, there, beneath her in the water, she saw the most beautiful young maiden she had ever seen. "Who are you?" she said, at the same moment the vision in the water said, "Who are you?" '

MARGARET: Oh — it was her!

CASH (motioning her to be silent): 'And at that moment she realised, yes, that it was her own reflection she was seeing! The pretty little girl of yesterday had grown into the beautiful young woman of today. And the king, like all of us who know about princesses, realised that his little Sweetie Pie had grown up — after all she was fast approaching her eighteenth birthday. He also knew that a beautiful princess deserves a handsome prince, so he sent for all the suitors in the land.'

(MARGARET runs forward in delight. CASH watches from his story-telling position.)

MARGARET: Eh, Anita, I'm going to get married.

ANITA (entering): Who to?

MARGARET: Oh, I don't know yet.

ANITA: Counting your chickens aren't you? Anyway what sort of a fella do you want?

MARGARET: Well, I don't really know — but me Dad says . . .

ANITA: Oh, what does he know about it! Come on, I'll soon help you to choose.

(They sit. FATHER enters.)

FATHER: Hello, Sweetie, Anita. Now then, love, you're going to meet quite a few young men before Mr Right comes along, but all you've got to remember is that I'm not having just anybody to take care of my Sweetie Pie . . .

CASH: Are we all ready, then, Mr King.

(CASH has placed a scoreboard in view. On it are the names of the contestants.)

FATHER (deferential): Oh, sorry, yes.

CASH: Right, then. First on our list is — Mr Arnold Smith.

(Enter A. SMITH, with brief-case and hat.)

SMITH: Good morning! My name is Arnold Smith and I'm in banking. I'm a bank clerk. My present situation is this: salary £1,200 which will be augmented by increments based on age, experience, length of service, responsibility and so on. A good superannuation scheme, generous pension at sixty. (ANITA yawns.)

FATHER (obviously impressed): And what are your views on marriage?

SMITH: As far as marriage is concerned a wife is an asset which would appreciate — I'm terribly sorry, which *I* would appreciate. She would be well provided for — I have, of course, a good life insurance policy.

FATHER: Hear that love.

ANITA (very bored): What do you do in the evenings?

SMITH: Well I do spend most evenings studying.

ANITA: Yes, I bet you do.

SMITH: It will pay dividends later. But I do make a point of setting aside Saturday for complete relaxation.

ANITA: What kind I wonder! (MARGARET giggles.)

CASH: Thank you, Mr Smith.

SMITH: Oh, thank you Sir. Good day. (He goes.)

ANITA: Blimey! What a creep.

FATHER: Nonsense. He's just the sort you need, Sweetie. He'll have all the exams and qualifications that your old Dad never had — he'll be able to provide for you as you deserve.

ANITA: Oh, but did you see how he was dressed. Looked like he just came out of the ark.

(MARGARET turns from one to the other, confused.)

FATHER: Now listen . . .

CASH (interrupts): Your score please, Mr King.

FATHER: What? Oh — nine. Yes, nine. (He glares at ANITA.)

(CASH writes the score up on the board.)

CASH: Sweetie?

MARGARET: Er . . . three.

CASH: Anita?

ANITA: One.

CASH: Well, the next candidate is Mr Dollery. Mr Philip . . .

(DINKIE DOLLERY bursts in, wearing a flashy tie.)

DOLLERY (interrupting CASH): Mr King isn't it? Pleased to meet you! I'm Dinkie Dollery. (He presents a card with his name etc. on it.) Well, you want to know a few details about yours truly. Pleased to! I'm a car sales executive but I'm fed up with being pushed around by the little men who won't expand their businesses — so when I get the finance worked out, I'll have a place of my own — a Car Mart.

FATHER: Is your job secure?

DOLLERY: Never sell yourself short, that's what I say; I sincerely believe it. If you don't have faith in yourself you'll be passed over.

ANITA: What kind of a car have you got?

DOLLERY: An MGBGT. I've known a lot of dollies — never been impressed before, but I know I'd be good for her — I'll be worth £10,000 before the year's out — not bad is it? Clothes from London, car of her own, fur coat . . .

ANITA (interrupting): I like yer tie.

CASH: Thank you Mr Dollery.

DOLLERY (to CASH): Oh, thank you. 20% off any new car. (He goes.)

ANITA: Oh, just imagine an MGBGT.

FATHER: You're not taken in by smooth talk like that are you? He'd bring you nothing but trouble, love. He won't be able to live on his wits for ever. (To CASH.) Nothing for me.

CASH: Margaret?

MARGARET: Two.

CASH: Anita?

ANITA: What? . . . Oh! — ten. Jackpot!

CASH: And our final contestant is Mr . . .

(ZOOT SIMS appears.)

ZOOT: Heh Man — don't come that name trip. (Looks around.) Wow — is this for *real*? Definitely not my scene — bad vibrations.

CASH: Mr . . . if you would kindly address Mr King . . .

ZOOT: O.K. man — let's get this thing together. Where's the chick? (Sees MARGARET.) Wow — too much — far out. Captain Cosmo — leader of the starship — take a trip with me babe. I'll show you the sunrise from the bottom of the sea. Dig it? Over and Out.

FATHER: Do you have a bank account or post office savings.

ZOOT: An illusion.

FATHER: What is your job and what are your plans for the future?

ZOOT: Zero minus — oh wow I'm blowing this gig. Time to split. Stay cool folks.

(He goes.)

ANITA: Hey, where did you get your beads?

CASH: Mr King.

FATHER: Nothing. (CASH notes the points on the board again.)

CASH: Sweetie?

MARGARET: . . . One.

ANITA: Zero minus man!

CASH: Thank you, ladies, Mr King; that was our final contestant for today.

FATHER: Well there's no argument is there? (He refers to the scoreboard.) The bank clerk seems a nice young man, love.

ANITA: What do you mean — she'd be bored off her head with him. Now listen, Margaret . . .

FATHER: He's a secure young man, love.

ANITA: Yes, flaming stuck-in-the-mud.

FATHER: You'll not go far wrong with him.

ANITA: I wouldn't go anywhere with him, specially dressed like that. If you really want to live a bit, you grab hold of that fella with the tie. You like cars don't you? Yes, she likes cars.

FATHER: Rubbish. He'd leave you high and dry.

ANITA: Fancy going into a pub with that bank fella. What would you feel like? She'd feel awful.

FATHER: She wouldn't. Would you, love? Course she wouldn't. Anyway we'll decide later, when we're on our own. (He goes.)

ANITA: Yeah, well I'm off now, but don't let him bully you into something you'll regret. Oh, imagine − an MGBGT. (She leaves.)

MARGARET: But Anita. I don't like any of them.

(BOB enters. He puts his hands over MARGARET's eyes.)

BOB: Three guesses!

MARGARET: Oh. Bob! Hiya.

BOB: My Mum wants to know if you'll come round Friday night to do her hair.

MARGARET: Yes, of course. Will you be there?

BOB: Yes. Look, what about coming out for a drink afterwards?

MARGARET (delighted): That would be great.

BOB: Well . . . see you Friday, then. (He goes. MARGARET gazes after him entranced.)

CASH: 'And so the Princess's heart was stolen, and in the coming days she would sit in her room, alone, except for her thoughts, dreaming about her very own Prince Charming.' Sweetie, do you like Bob?

MARGARET: I think he's sweet.

CASH: But what does Bob think of you? Are you the girl of his dreams, the girl he'd be proud to show his friends − or are you the little girl he's always known? Don't look so worried, Sweetie. I will solve all your problems. I've got a present for you: a woman's constant companion − her magazine. (He hands her a woman's magazine.)

MARGARET: Oh, thank you, Mrs Cash. (She reads the titles from the magazine.) 'A day with Tom Jones' . . . 'Knit him a sweater' . . . 'Cooking on a budget' . . . this is it − 'New Look for the Autumn Girl'.

(MARGARET reads from the magazine as the FASHION EDITOR (female) and ASSISTANT (male) enter. They are planning the issue she is reading.)

EDITOR: Now then, summer's over, let's hit them big with a completely new look for Autumn.

ASSISTANT: Right! Colours. Last year we played safe, brown, green, Autumn shades, so I decided 'Autumn Girl 72' will experiment with purples and yellows.

EDITOR: Yes. A complete change of wardrobe from the summer pastels.

ASSISTANT: Right. And the photos will all suggest Autumn snugness, security, warmth: models curled up by log fires — the usual sort of thing.

MARGARET: 'How to be a sex kitten!'

EDITOR: Skirt lengths. Now the tights manufacturers won't like it, but I think we'll keep in with the rag trade and have skirts even longer than last year. Fits in with the cosiness too.

ASSISTANT: Maxi skirts, long boots and er . . . Tam o' Shanters. Yes, jaunty angle for the new daring Autumn girl.

(CASH hands MARGARET a Tam o' Shanter.)

MARGARET: I wonder if one of those would suit me? (She puts it on.)

EDITOR: Now, are we going to put the accent on keeping your summer tan or getting a new pale look?

ASSISTANT: Keep it. It'll go with the new colours and anyway we could use the article 'Overnight Tans' we left out of the May issue. Yes, the tawny look. Rouge and brighter lipsticks.

EDITOR: O.K. So we'll go all out for grooming and health. A feature on deodorants and some exercises for keeping your summer fitness.

ASSISTANT: What sort of pose should our Autumn girl portray?

EDITOR: She stands with legs apart.

ASSISTANT: Head held high.

EDITOR: Hands on hips.

ASSISTANT: With hips thrust forward. (MARGARET follows the directions into a very awkward pose.)

EDITOR: Super darling. (Deferential.) Is that all right, Mr Cash?

CASH: Yes, fine. It'll sell well. Next month I want this lot scrapped and a hard sell on the gay, glittering, party girl image. Right?

EDITOR & ASSISTANT: Yes Mr Cash. Lovely Mr Cash. Thank you Mr Cash. (They go.)

(MARGARET comes to and sits down to listen again.)

CASH: 'And the princess's preparations were rewarded, for no sooner had Robert caught sight of her than his heart stood still. He was soon to be seen constantly at her side, paying her compliments and speaking the tenderest of words.

'One midsummer eve, Robert decided the time had come to ask the King for his daughter's hand in marriage. The King called the joyous couple to him; he gave them his blessing and officially declared them betrothed.'

(MARGARET sits entranced.)

Come on, Sweetie; there's lots to do before the great day.

(MARGARET's MOTHER comes in, carrying a jigsaw puzzle on a tray.)

MOTHER: Now, if I can find this bit of sky, this corner will be finished. The trouble is they all look the same.

(MARGARET and BOB enter. MARGARET is carrying some curtain material.)

MARGARET: Don't you think it's a lovely colour, Bob?

MOTHER: Oh hello, Bob . . .

BOB: Mrs King.

MOTHER: . . . there are some more presents for you to look at.

MARGARET: It'll go well with the carpet, love, and it was ever so cheap on the market.

BOB: Yes, it's very nice. Shall we go then, Margaret?

MARGARET (quickly): Oh, I thought we'd stay in tonight; it's pouring down.

BOB: But I've got my Dad's car.

MARGARET: But there are a lot more presents you haven't seen yet.

MOTHER: Yes, sit down for a bit, Bob. Margaret love, I'm stuck again. Come and give me a hand.

MARGARET (moving to MOTHER): Oh, Mum, you've put that in the wrong place. Let's spread the pieces out more. We could get this finished tonight.

BOB: Margaret — it's not often that I get the car.

MOTHER: I should have thought you'd be wanting to save as much as you can, Bob. And anyway, what is there to do on a Tuesday?

BOB: I could think of plenty, couldn't you Margaret?

MARGARET: There's another bit of sky. I bet Bob'll like that coffee pot from Auntie Peggy, don't you Mum? And guess what — another toaster arrived today, Bob.

BOB: Well, we'll be able to have breakfast in bed then, won't we?

MOTHER (with a piece of jigsaw): Oh no, that won't do.

MARGARET: Well it means Georgina didn't read the list. Oh Mum, what else was it that Bob had to do? The bridesmaids' presents, the . . .

BOB (interrupting): . . . the taxis, the flowers, the ushers — I know all that, we've heard nothing else for months: the train tickets, the hotel, the double room, the double bed . . .

MOTHER (cutting in): Stop fooling about, Bob: save that sort of talk for your stag night please. It's no good, I'll never find this bit of sky without my glasses. (She goes out.)

BOB: Come on, love, let's get out. (He goes over to her.)

MARGARET: Just leave me alone. And stop that smutty talk in front of my mother.

BOB: Smutty! Look, all I want is for you to leave this bloody jigsaw and come for a ride in the car . . .

MARGARET (interrupting): Yes, and the rest. I don't want a repeat of last Saturday, thank you.

BOB: But you wanted me on Saturday: I know you did. Listen, you know I won't force you but I love you Margaret and I want to sleep with you. If you want to sleep with me, there's nothing to stop us.

MARGARET: I've told you: I don't want a repeat of last Saturday.

MOTHER (coming back): You'll stay for your supper, Bob, won't you? I've put some sausage rolls in the oven. (She sits down.) That's better, I can see what I'm doing now. Oh, Margaret, Mrs Watson's coming round with our Angela's bridesmaid's dress tomorrow, and she wants a fitting with you at the same time. So we don't want to see you here, Bob: can't see the bride's dress before the great day! Oh, I've got rid of that piece at last. I always feel sorry for Mabel Watson, you know: she's made beautiful dresses for so many girls and then her own daughter went and disgraced herself and had to get married in a registry office.

BOB: There was a young waitress called Mabel,
Whose morals were very unstable . . .

MARGARET: Shut up, Bob.

(MOTHER becomes occupied picking up some jigsaw pieces that have been dropped.)

BOB (in a loud whisper): . . . The head waiter called Dan
   Said, 'Give us a bang',
   And they were at it all night on the table!

MARGARET: Shut up you!

MOTHER (emerging): No wonder we couldn't get on: there were all these
   pieces on the floor. Margaret, go and bring the supper in.

MARGARET (furious with BOB): It'd be a pleasure.

BOB (catching her arm): Listen Margaret . . .

MOTHER: Oh, I can take a hint. Two's company . . . (She goes out.)

MARGARET: Let me go, you're hurting. And if you think that kind of
   joke's funny, well I just think it's disgusting. Yes, I did want you on
   Saturday night, but God knows why if it's all such a bloody joke to
   you.

BOB: You know that's not . . .

MARGARET (losing her temper): Do you think I've got no feelings?
   Don't you realise that I'm fed up with all this too: bridesmaids'
   dresses, present lists, making curtains, never going out, my mother
   and her stupid jigsaws. (She throws the jigsaw on the floor.) And
   what if I got pregnant? I don't suppose that even entered your head.
   Well, I've worried myself sick at the thought of it: that's why I won't
   sleep with you and that's why I daren't come out with you tonight.

   (Pause.)

BOB (crossing to her and holding her): I know, love.

MARGARET: I thought it'd be great being engaged but we don't seem
   to get any time together. And when I am with you, I just find myself
   wanting to do things that I know are wrong. Anyway, I want it to be
   something special, not in the back of a car.

BOB: I know you do. Look, I'm sorry about that joke.

MARGARET: Oh forget it. I've been pretty rotten myself.

BOB: That's what your mum'll say when she sees her jigsaw.

MARGARET: Bob! She'll go mad. (She starts to pick up the pieces,
   giggling.) She's been doing this for a week. Come on, help me, Bob.

BOB: Right. Ten bits of sky coming up. (He bends to help her and
   whispers:) Hope she doesn't come in and catch us on the floor together!

MARGARET: Yes, and as soon as her back's turned!

BOB: Well, don't think I won't tell how this got knocked down: 'She
   attacked me in a fit of mad passion, Mrs King, and your jigsaw just
   happened to be in the way'. (They roll on the floor, laughing.)

BOB (pulling her up): How about skipping supper and going for a drink? We could walk down, no car.

MARGARET: You're joking. I'm not walking in this weather — we'll go in the car. (They leave.)

(Peal of bells, wedding march. These and the following sermon cover the entrances into church of BOB, MARGARET's MOTHER and lastly, MARGARET, radiant on her FATHER's arm.)

CASH (as Clergyman, reading): 'Dearly beloved, we are gathered here today in the sight of God, and in the face of this congregation, to join together this Man and this Woman in Holy Matrimony. First, it was ordained for the procreation of children, to be brought up in the fear of the Lord. Secondly, a remedy against sin, and to avoid fornication; that such persons as have not the gift of continency might marry and keep themselves undefiled members of Christ's body. Thirdly, for the mutual society, help, and comfort, that one ought to have of the other, both in prosperity and adversity.
'Who giveth this Woman to be married to this Man?

(MARGARET is handed from her father to BOB.)

'O well is thee, and happy shalt thou be.
Thy wife shall be as the fruitful vine upon the walls of thine house.
Thy children like the olive-branches round about thy table.
Lo, thus shall the man be blessed.
And as it was in the beginning, is now, and ever shall be,
world without end. Amen.'

(MARGARET and BOB go.)

MOTHER: This is the happiest day of my life. (MOTHER and FATHER leave.)

CASH (as himself): 'And so they were married and lived happily ever after.' (He closes the book.) And that, ladies and gentlemen, is the end of my story.

MARGARET (rushing in with the veil on her head): The end! You must be joking! I've only just got married.

CASH: Sweetie — you're nineteen, you've just got married. What more could a young girl want?

MARGARET: I want another story. (She takes the book.) That was a good one. There's a lot more in here. Ooh, look at this . . .

CASH (sharply): Margaret!

MARGARET: And this . . .

CASH (furiously): Margaret!!

(MARGARET sulkily hands back the book. She sits down.)

MARGARET (determined): Well, I'm not leaving here till you read me another story. (She changes to a coy, wheedling tone, fluttering her eyelashes.) . . . Please . . .

CASH: Very well then. The next story is about the princess's life as the ideal wife: how she cooks and cleans . . .

MARGARET: There are a few things I'm worried about there.

CASH: We'll have to take a few lessons then. (He goes out with the book.)

(Enter JOAN.)

JOAN: Oh, is he not here yet? Thank goodness. I ran all the way from the bus. I've just got my honeymoon snaps back.

MARGARET: How long have you been married?

JOAN: Six weeks on Saturday.

MARGARET: Oh, that's nice.

JOAN: Have you done your homework?

MARGARET: Yes, it was easy wasn't it?

JOAN: Oh, it took me ages. I thought it was right difficult . . .

(Enter CASH.)

CASH: Good morning, ladies.

MARGARET & JOAN: Good morning, sir.

CASH: And how are my ideal wives today?

MARGARET & JOAN: Very well, thank you sir.

CASH (motioning them to sit): That's what I like to hear. Can't have any of my ladies under the weather, can I? Well now, I think it's time we had a look at all we've learnt so far on the ideal wife course — No need to look so worried, ladies: they'll all be questions we'll be proud to answer. So — Topic Number 1: Politics. Sweetie, what do you know about Politics?

MARGARET: Nothing really . . .

CASH: Good! Keep it that way. A Good Wife, while not . . .

(As he talks, MARGARET takes out a bag of sweets and leans over to JOAN.)

MARGARET: Do you want a toffee?

CASH (his flow interrupted, shouts): Margaret! We do not offer sweets round when we're talking about Politics.

MARGARET: But I've just told you, I don't know anything about Politics.

CASH: But you *do* know how to behave when a man is about to make an important statement.

JOAN (eager to please): You stop what you're doing and listen.

CASH: Exactly! Now, Joan perhaps you can tell us what *you* know about unions.

JOAN (stands and recites): My husband will probably belong to a union. I won't complain if he has to go to meetings with his mates — as long as it doesn't end in strikes.

CASH: And why's that?

MARGARET (leaping forward): Because it's irresponsible strike action that's bringing this country to it's knees.

CASH: Well done, Sweetie! The emotion's coming on nicely. (They sit.) Now ladies, the place where you really do come into your own — the *kitchen.* (As though starting a race.) Ready? Off you go.

JOAN: Always start him off with a good breakfast.

MARGARET: Ask his mother for his favourite recipes.

JOAN: Always make a meal look attractive.

MARGARET: Don't complain about the time it took.

JOAN: Leave your apron in the kitchen.

MARGARET: An empty plate is thanks enough.

JOAN: Make sure his meals are ready when he wants them.

MARGARET (stops short, forgetting the 'race'): But suppose he comes in late or . . .

CASH (interrupts): A good wife copes with all eventualities: is *queen* of her kitchen. (Smugly.) Cooking is a pleasure; service with a smile.

MARGARET (impatient): Oh, I know all that, but supposing . . .

CASH (exasperated): All right, Sweetie Pie — a few tears in the first few months but then dry your eyes and persevere: if a job's worth doing, it's worth doing well. And, of course, this particular job *is* worth doing well because . . . (He conducts their reply.) . . .

MARGARET & JOAN: . . . The way to a man's heart is through his stomach.

CASH: Beautifully said! (MARGARET bursts into giggles as he stands entranced. He comes to abruptly.) To continue, Margaret. Repairs and Maintenance. Number 1: Clothes.

JOAN (mechanically) & MARGARET (faltering and copying JOAN): We wash, we sew, we iron, we mend.

CASH: Furniture.

MARGARET & JOAN: We arrange, we dust, we polish, we tend.

CASH: Floors.

MARGARET & JOAN: We sweep, we hoover, we scrub and bend.

CASH: Electrics.

MARGARET (seizing her chance as JOAN falls silent): We find the fuse wire and . . .

CASH: Ah! Ah! It's a trick question, Sweetie.

MARGARET: But I . . .

CASH: And no 'buts'. Let me see the plugs I gave you to mend over the weekend.

(They both take plugs out of their baskets and hold them up. JOAN's is a complete mess, MARGARET'S looks like a new plug and flex.)

CASH (taking JOAN's): Excellent Joan. Your husband *is* going to have fun sorting that out for his little wife, isn't he? (He comes to MARGARET's plug.) Margaret! What *have* you done?

MARGARET: Well I took it to bits and then . . .

CASH (shouting): Take it to bits by all means but you didn't have to put it back together again did you?

MARGARET: Well, what's the point of taking it to bits then?

CASH: *That* is not going to show Bob how much you need him is it? Just don't do it again. USE YOUR HEAD! (He recovers himself.) Oh dear me, girls, you're going to make me grey before my time at this rate. (He laughs, so they laugh.) Well let's see if we can all get the next question right. *Party time.* Your husband tells a clean joke. What do you do?

MARGARET & JOAN: We laugh admiringly.

CASH: Your husband tells a naughty joke?

MARGARET & JOAN: We giggle.

CASH: He tells a really dirty one?

MARGARET & JOAN: We frown.

CASH: Because?

MARGARET & JOAN: When the boys are blue, the girls are pink!

CASH: Bravo! . . . And speaking of blue and pink − *babies*!

MARGARET & JOAN (ecstatically): Ooh! Aah! (Etc.)

CASH (cutting in): Ladies! I salute you. And need I, a mere male, say more? I think we can safely leave baby care to those wonderful maternal instincts of yours. (All are rapt.) Now, maternal instincts are one thing but driving instincts are another. Margaret, do you want to learn to drive the car?

MARGARET: We haven't got a car — we can't afford it. Wish we could.

CASH: No, Sweetie, *imagine* you've got one.

MARGARET: Oh, I see. Well I wouldn't mind a Capri.

CASH: There's no need to remember *names*. Just remember that you don't want to drive.

JOAN: Well, your husband would always need the car in any case.

CASH: Quite. And anyway, all those horrible things to remember — double declutching, reversing, three-point turns and those nasty yellow lines — are much better left to the men aren't they?

MARGARET & JOAN: Yes sir.

CASH: And no back seat driving. And if something goes wrong under the bonnet?

MARGARET (triumphantly remembering the plug, she shoots up hand): Take it to bits and leave it in bits!

CASH (walks up to her, controlling himself with difficulty): We don't even TOUCH it, Margaret!

JOAN: Just say you don't know how he understands all those complicated pipes.

CASH: That's my girl. Now what have we next. (He consults the revision list.) Ah yes! (Clearing his throat and lowering his voice.) Our — um — our — er — 'private' relationships with our husbands. (They look embarrassed.) Well, let's just say we leave that up to them. One or two quick words of advice though — always live up to *his* expectations and always assure him he lives up to *yours*. Yes, you'll not go far wrong with that as a motto.

(MARGARET, puzzled, puts up her hand.)

Hand down please, Margaret. Well, that's as far as we'll go today I think. Tomorrow we'll revise money matters, gardening, religion and The Other Woman. (MARGARET and JOAN are horrorstruck.) No, don't look so worried, ladies, The Other Woman is no match for the Ideal Wife and that's what we're all going to be, isn't it?

MARGARET & JOAN: Yes sir.

CASH: Till tomorrow then. Au revoir, ladies. (He goes.)

MARGARET & JOAN: Good morning, sir.

(They start to leave.)

JOAN (dreamy): What a wonderful man!

MARGARET (worried): I didn't do so well today, did I?

JOAN (bitchy): Well . . .

MARGARET: I suppose it's bound to take a few months.

(JOAN goes. MARGARET notices the storybook on its stand. Looking round to make sure no one is watching, she goes up to it and starts peeping into the book.)

MARGARET: Ooh!! 'SWEETIE AND THE HAPPY EVENT.' 'Margaret sat cross-legged on the ottoman . . . '

(Enter CASH.)

CASH: Margaret. That is naughty!

MARGARET (startled): I was just reading what happens.

CASH: Oh I see. My reading isn't good enough for you any more.

MARGARET: Oh no!! It's much better when you read it. Go on, read this one.

CASH: Very well. (To the audience.) She can twist me around her little finger. (To MARGARET.) Comfy? Good.
'SWEETIE AND THE HAPPY EVENT.'
'Margaret sat cross-legged on the ottoman, her shoulders huddled into the warmth of the tumbling curtains — her face pressed cold against the glass. She tried hard to think but her emotions kept swelling in her mind and overflowing. She had tried so hard not to cry but now her strength was gone and tears rolled half-pace down her smooth skin and fell to form small pools of joyful sadness on the window-sill. She was a woman. No longer a girl — no longer a newly-wed, but a woman. Without knowing she moved her hands across the smooth flat area that hid the secret new life within her.
'The gentle click told her that Bob was already closing the door behind him. She raced into the large Georgian parlour and Bob looked at her. As always she felt weak at the realisation that Bob loved her so deeply. She moved closer to him and opened her soft lips to release her secret into sharing. No sound came, only a happy sigh — but she could tell from the proud eyes and the smiling lips moving down to hers that there was no need for words. She sank into his strong arms and knew that no woman could be more fulfilled. Yes — she was a woman.' (He closes the book.)

MARGARET (sighing): Ooh . . .

CASH: And now Sweetie, I have a present for you. (He hands her a wrapped parcel. She unwraps a baby catalogue.)

MARGARET: Oh! 'Mumsie-care.' Thanks very much. Bob, I'd love a coach-built pram.

CASH: Miss Forsythe!

BOB (entering): How much is it? £35! — We could get one second-hand.

(A shop assistant, MISS FORSYTHE, comes forward.)

MISS FORSYTHE: Oh! Not for our first baby sir. It *is* our first baby, isn't it? Yes, I can tell by the glow. (To MARGARET.) Men just don't understand these things.

BOB: Well, we'd never get that on a bus.

MARGARET: Don't be daft, we'll need a carry-cot as well.

MISS FORSYTHE: And we have some lovely ones here, madam. These leather ones are the . . .

MARGARET (seeing BOB's expression): Well, these plastic ones look very nice.

MISS FORSYTHE: If you're not buying to last, I suppose . . . Madam, will you just look at these cradles. Aren't they too adorable for words? With appropriate trimmings for boys and girls. (Seeing MARGARET's worried expression.) Well, who could deny their baby one of these?

MARGARET: I think one of these big cots would be best because the baby can sleep in that for two years.

MISS FORSYTHE: Indeed he can: with pretty transfers, drop down sides and non-toxic paint for perfect safety. And, of course, we have bedding to match.

MARGARET: Those quilts are pretty.

MISS FORSYTHE: And sheets, blankets and pillow-cases in the same colours.

MARGARET: I was wondering about nappies.

MISS FORSYTHE: We're going to need plenty of them, aren't we? These disposable ones are . . .

MARGARET: No, no, Carol next door says they don't keep as much in.

MISS FORSYTHE: They do if we buy the best brands, madam. Three packets to try? And a dozen of the towelling ones just in case.

BOB: Dirty little thing. Don't expect me to do any of the washing.

MARGARET: You do your job, I'll do mine.

MISS FORSYTHE: Then clothing, madam. We have a large selection here. From babies, through toddlers to tiny tots. And sterilisers, feeding bottles, potties, baby bouncers, play-pens, toys and we mustn't forget — *mother*, must we? (In a hushed voice.) We have some lovely sleep and support bras, with moisture-proof pads. (Louder.) So if you follow me we'll get you a few snazzy smocks. (MARGARET and MISS

FORSYTHE go out.)

CASH (as Salesman): One hundred and thirty pounds please, Mr Johnson.

BOB: Christ. That's a bit steep isn't it?

CASH: The cost of bliss, Mr Johnson, the cost of bliss.

BOB: But a hundred and thirty quid's worth?

CASH: Think of the happiness it will bring your good lady wife, and think of yourself Mr Johnson. Think of all the hours you will spend keeping your son away from his train set. Well it's been a pleasure doing business with you Mr Johnson. I hope we see you again very soon. Good day. (BOB goes.)

(CAROL enters.)

MARGARET (off): Carol!

CAROL: Oh, hello, love. Come in. Eh, what's the matter with you. Are you all right?

MARGARET: I've just been to the doctor's . . .

CAROL: It's not the baby?

MARGARET: He examined me and he says I'm having twins.

CAROL: You're not! Twins! Eh, you'd better sit down. Still I'm not surprised, the size you are.

MARGARET: I don't know what Bob's going to say.

CAROL: Doesn't he know yet, then?

MARGARET: No, and it's only this week we put that deposit on the pram.

CAROL: Course! You'll need one of them twin prams, won't you? Eh I like them. You'll need two of everything. I'll have to get knitting, girl!!

MARGARET: Yes, but it's going to be ever so expensive; we were a bit shocked at the cost of things, anyway. Bob keeps saying we should have been more careful.

CAROL: Oh . . . it wasn't actually planned? . . . Well, whose is? I wonder what they'll be — boys or girls. You know what they say: big in the belly means girls, big in the bottom means boys.

MARGARET: I think I'd like one of each; I expect Bob would like two boys.

CAROL: Well, they are more affectionate . . . little devils.

MARGARET: You see, it's just that we're not used to living on one wage. I could have kept working longer if I hadn't been so sick.

CAROL: I'll tell you what. I've got some things left over from my three upstairs. There's nothing wrong with them. I'd have offered them before, but you were so set on having everything new.

MARGARET: Well I was, but I never expected twins. I'd be very glad of them if you're sure you don't mind.

CAROL: Not at all. I'll go and get them now. (Calling from off-stage.) Do twins run in your family?

MARGARET: Not in mine, they don't.

CAROL (returning with a small suit-case): Well you check up on Bob's. I bet they do. You can insure against them, you know. You'll have to do that next time. Now what have we got in here? There's some nappies for a start — you'll want plenty of them. (She hands them to MARGARET. CAROL notices the congratulation cards.) Oh, look at these. They're the ones I got last time. (She reads out a sentimental verse from one card.) I had our Deborah at Townleys, you know.

MARGARET: Carol, there was a woman at the clinic this morning who was three days in labour with her first baby — do you think it could be even longer with twins?

CAROL: I don't know, love. It all depends on the person. Look at me, my third took the longest and I had to have ten stitches. Eh, there must be two cords. Well, I hope it's the lad who comes out first, 'cos they say 'First out is the most intelligent'. (She holds one of the garments up.) Oh, doesn't this look tiny? You'd never think our Peter could have got into this, would you?

MARGARET: That's pretty. We'll have to think of some more names.

CAROL: I wonder if they'll be identical. Well, if they're girls they'd better not favour Bob! Did he tell you, I was teasing him in the pub the other night? Told him the barmaid had her eye on him.

MARGARET: He's been ever so good, you know. He brought me a cup of tea in bed this morning.

CAROL: Oh, you'll have to keep that up. And you stay in hospital as long as you can — you'll have enough to do when you come home. Let's have a look and see if this is stained. (She unfolds a shawl; they hold it between them and fold it up again.)

MARGARET: It's going to be ever so difficult feeding them isn't it? Do you think you have more milk with twins?

CAROL: I don't know, love. Anyway, you can always supplement with bottles. Oh, I don't envy you in the middle of the night.

MARGARET: I hope they don't cry a lot. We both like our sleep.

CAROL: Trouble is they'll set each other off. Don't worry, love, they'll be company for each other later on. Now if you give me this lot, I'll pack them up and carry them round for you — you mustn't go carrying anything heavy.

MARGARET: They say I might have to go in a bit early because of my blood pressure . . .

(They go out.)

CASH (reading): 'Time flies and Margaret's radiance grows with each passing day. Bob's mind runs a never-ending relay race between pride and concern for his beloved wife. At last the happy day arrives and Margaret's maternal longings are fulfilled. Soon the house is full of hustle and bustle, the paraphernalia that children bring; the rhymes, the games of hop, skip and jump fill the air.'

CASH & WOMAN (singing as if on the radio):
What shall we do?
Let's play a game,
Let's do something now.

CASH: We play cowboys

WOMAN: We play dolls.

BOTH: We don't like your game.

(MARGARET comes on, pushing a table with ironing on it. She sits at the table. Noise of children off-stage.)

CASH (singing):
Boys should build things,
Play with cars,
Break a few windows,
Learn to be hard,
Collect some spiders,
Steal some fruit,
Get their knees dirty in the yard.

(During the song MARGARET puts on her apron, rolls up her sleeves etc.)

WOMAN:
Little girls should learn to
Care for their clothes,
Look after their dolls
And blow their nose.
They should be gentle
And neat and sweet and nice,
'Cos they're made from sugar and spice.

BOTH (as before): What shall we do . . . (They repeat the verse.)

WOMAN: Now children, Uncle Ben is going to tell you how to make a toy duck. (CASH as Uncle Ben, murmurs instructions behind the following scene: ' . . . glue . . . felt . . . Daddy's pipe-cleaners . . . ')

(Noise of children playing off-stage. The level should be raised and lowered as necessary during the scene.)

MARGARET (going to the garden door and calling to the children): Now you two, play nicely and let Mummy get on with her work. No Jane, love, leave your ribbon in, it looks pretty; and, Tommy, we'll have to get your hair cut before your Dad comes home — he'll be saying you look like a girl! (To herself.) He would have to be the one with the curls! (Looking round at the room.) What a mess! I'll get this lot out of the way first. (She starts to iron.) And he didn't eat his egg this morning; he'll never be big and strong. And what about the waste! Eggs have gone up twopence this week, and milk's dearer too. I don't know how Bob expects me to manage.

(There is a knock at the door.)

Now who's that?

POSTMAN (stepping in): Good morning, Mrs Johnson. Parcel for you, love. Sign here, please.

MARGARET (signs): Oh it's for the kids. That's nice. Thanks very much.

POSTMAN: Good morning. (Goes.)

MARGARET: Tommy and Jane there's a parcel here from your granny; you can open it later if you're good: no, I said 'Later', if you're good . . . well then, Jane, give him his gun back; no wonder he's being naughty.

(There is another knock at the door.)

MARGARET: Oh dear . . . (She turns back in the direction of the children.) What's that now? For heaven's sake keep that racket down!

MILKMAN (entering): Morning, love, and a fine one it is, too. (MARGARET takes two bottles.) That's 70 pence please, love.

MARGARET: Oh, is it Friday? (She pays him and rushes off.)

MILKMAN: What's the matter with you, love? Your husband on nights? (Goes.)

CASH (as if on the radio): Now children, it's time for another story from Auntie Sally. Today's story is called 'Mary Visits her Grandma' — Auntie Sally.

WOMAN (as Auntie Sally): Hello children! 'One day Mary woke up bright and early and said to Mummy, "Can I go and see Grandma?" "Of course," said Mummy. So hopping on the little red train, Mary went chuff, chuff, chuff, off to see Granny. When she got there Granny

said, "My, am I glad to see you. I'm in the middle of spring-cleaning
and a little girl like you is just the one to help me." So, getting out
Granny's feather dusters, they soon had the house looking spick and
span . . . ' (She continues to murmur this story during the Book
Salesman scene.)

SALESMAN (entering): Good morning! Mrs Johnson, I believe. Not too
busy to answer a few questions?

MARGARET: Well . . .

SALESMAN: Let me introduce myself. I represent an educational
research organisation — offices near the Town Hall — and we are
currently involved in a study of pre-school children.

MARGARET: Oh, well, would you like to sit down?

SALESMAN: Thank you. Now, you have two children, I believe?

MARGARET: Yes.

SALESMAN (filling in a form): What are their ages?

MARGARET: Four. They're twins.

SALESMAN: Really? A delightful age, isn't it? What is your husband's
occupation, Mrs Johnson?

MARGARET: He's a maintenance electrician.

SALESMAN: 'Maintenance Electrician' — good. Your children have
started to read have they?

MARGARET: Oh, they're only four — (The SALESMAN starts to write.)
— but I was hoping to —

SALESMAN: Don't worry — they'll catch up. That's where a concerned
parent like you can help. Are you a trained teacher?

MARGARET: No.

SALESMAN: Pity . . . You do read to them, of course?

MARGARET: Well, they get a comic every week, and . . .

SALESMAN: I see. Well, it is important to encourage the right *kind* of
reading from the start — it can make all the difference to their chances
later on. Please let me introduce you to this volume. I've found it
invaluable with my own two. It's based on the most up-to-date
American research. It's been compiled by an experienced team of
educational psychologists, and, as you can see, the written text is
supported by visual material at every stage.

MARGARET: How much is it?

SALESMAN: Well, this is the first of a thirty volume set. But we give it
to you absolutely free of charge, providing, of course, you accept the

rest of the set at a very reasonable two pounds the volume.

MARGARET: Well, I'd have to see Bob, my husband, about it first . . .

SALESMAN: Of course, though if you were to sign right away, I could allow you the twenty five per cent discount, bringing the price down to just one pound fifty per volume. The form is already completed . . .

MARGARET: I don't know . . .

SALESMAN: Tell you what – I'll pop by on my way past tomorrow morning! Then we can see what you, and Bob, have decided. And please allow me to leave you with this: 'Education begins at home', which is designed to answer any questions you may have, and to enable you, the parent, to use this Course to your child's best advantage. Right, see you tomorrow, then. Thank you again, Mrs Johnson – you have been most helpful.

WOMAN (on radio): '. . . So proudly holding the bag of cakes she and Granny had made, she hopped on the little red train, waved goodbye to Granny and went chuff, chuff, chuff back home to Mummy; and very soon she was tucked up safe in bed. What a lovely day it had been!'

CASH (on radio): Did you enjoy that children? That's all we have time for today. Don't forget to sit down with Mummy at the same time tomorrow. Bye, Bye.

Now, ladies, it is time for Talk Around for today. And today we are very privileged to have in our studio that well-known columnist and journalist – Marjorie Proops. Hello Marjorie.

M. PROOPS: Hello.

CASH: Now today, Marjorie is going to give you ladies some advice on how to keep your man away from The Other Woman. Marjorie.

(During the following monologue, MARGARET puts away the ironing things, listening attentively to the radio.)

M. PROOPS: Well one main piece of advice, ladies – never give him the chance to go near The Other Woman. Almost any wife can adopt mistress tactics. For instance, why not scatter a few girlie magazines about the house, or, if he fancies himself as a tearaway in the kitchen, say how much you enjoy washing-up after one of his super-do's – leave the washing-up till morning. Agree that Match of the Day is, indeed, compulsive T.V. viewing – say how strange it is that those Soccer players make you feel so sexy and how nice it is that he is even sexier than any of them. Suggest making love on a Sunday afternoon – if he says, 'You must be joking', tell him you'll show him what a joker you really are. Show him. Now that's Sundays ladies, what about tonight? Very soon your husband is going to walk through the front door, tired out after a hard day at the office. Is it going to be another boring old Monday evening or are you going to make it into a special occasion? Just go over to the mirror and have a look at yourself — (MARGARET moves over to an imaginary mirror.) — not very inspiring is it?

MARGARET: You're not kidding!

M. PROOPS: If you really want to excite your man as he comes through the door why don't you wear one of his shirts, black tights, high-heeled shoes and a pinny or — if you're really daring — just a pinny.

(MARGARET hesitates, then quickly unbuttons her blouse and takes it off, revealing an ordinary bra. She fluffs up her hair, admires herself in the mirror, but becomes self-conscious when she hears BOB coming. He enters, whistling.)

MARGARET: Bob! Is that you?

(BOB stares, holds the pause.)

BOB: The kettle's boiling.

(MARGARET goes out and comes back in with two cups of tea. She tries to regain her sexy pose.)

MARGARET: Do you want a cup of tea, darling?

BOB: What are you doing with no blouse on?

(MARGARET, humiliated, drags on her blouse.)

We had a meeting of the shop in the yard this afternoon . . .

(MARGARET rushes out.)

MARGARET (off): Tommy, Tommy, come on the two of you, come in — get up these stairs and get in that bath — Tommy put that down — I'm warning you, Tommy. (The sound of a slap. She comes in.) So help me I'll bloody murder him. (She throws a toy across the room.)

BOB: What do you want to hit him like that for? He was only playing with his toys.

MARGARET: It's all right for you, you're not at home all day. Do you know what he did this morning? He went into Mrs Murphy's garden and ruined her flower-bed. Thank goodness it's nearly our holidays.

BOB: We're not going on holiday, love — I'm on strike, it's unofficial — so there's no money.

MARGARET: Oh Bob, you can't.

BOB: Don't you start — we can and have.

MARGARET: You're just the same as all the rest — sheep following them Commies.

BOB: It's nowt to do with bloody Commies — we're after a better standard of living.

MARGARET: You don't deserve a job at all if you neglect your family!

BOB: That's a typical woman's attitude. You don't know the first thing about it — but you go on and on just the same.

MARGARET: Well I'm the one who suffers — I've got to find the food. I don't understand you at all. The firm offered you a 6% rise next April but no, you won't accept that, you've got to try and ruin the firm and the whole country too. Well, that's it. I'll have to get a job.

BOB: You bloody won't.

MARGARET: I can put the kids in a nursery, and the money I earn can keep us going until you're back at work — then I can put it towards our savings.

BOB: Look, for a start I'm not having my kids in a home — and my wife is not going to work in a factory.

MARGARET: They're not homes, Bob — they're very good for children, they learn a lot at three and four. And it doesn't have to be a factory job. (Quite enthusiastic.) I could be a shop assistant.

BOB: I said NO — I mean NO!

MARGARET: Think what it would mean, Bob! We'd have more money — the twins would know more when they go to school. (Pause.) And anyway, I've been thinking about it for a long time. I've got to get out of the house more. I'm stuck here all day. I'm only 24, Bob, and I spend my time doing the same things day in and day out.

BOB: Look, I'm sorry love. I know the kids can be a bit of a handful. Tell you what — go up and get them settled and then we'll open that bottle of wine my Dad bought us.

MARGARET: You can't put me off with a bottle of wine, Bob — I'm determined. (She goes.)

BOB: Women!

CASH: You can't expect me to have any sympathy, Bob. It's no wonder the women are getting annoyed; the men are letting them down and you are letting Margaret down. Now you've got a good wife there, Bob. She looks after you, your children, your house. She cooks and cleans, and now you're forcing her to think that she has to go out and earn the money as well; it isn't natural, Bob.

BOB: That's what I kept telling her, but she's dead set on the idea.

CASH: No she isn't, she's just desperate at the moment. Look, you keep your half of the bargain and go back to work, and she'll be only too pleased that things are back to normal.

BOB: I've got to stand by my mates. We want more money for our families.

CASH: You're cutting your own throat Bob. The firm will give you the money when times are better. All you're doing is dragging production right down. Nothing was ever gained by holding the country to ransom. You remember that. Now off you go. (BOB goes.) And send Margaret in. (She enters.) Hello Margaret. It's been a hard day hasn't it? (No reply.) Don't worry, you'll be all right again soon.

MARGARET: Nothing like this ever happens in the stories, does it?

CASH: I've been thinking, Sweetie . . . about what you were saying . . . Bob and the strike . . . and I'm sure you're right. There are Communists trying to lead good men like Bob astray; but your going out to work isn't going to help, Sweetie . . . (MARGARET turns away impatiently.)

CASH: And think of the children. Think of them spending all day with strangers who can't possibly care as much as you do.

MARGARET: I think they'd *like* to go to a nursery; they tie me up in knots with their questions . . . They need somebody who's qualified to teach them.

CASH: Sweetie! There is no substitute for a mother. Any psychologist will tell you that a child deprived of its mother's care and attention in the formative years becomes maladjusted and delinquent. You don't want that, do you?

MARGARET: They'll be delinquent anyway, the way I nag at them . . . I'm desperate to get away from them sometimes . . .

CASH: Oh!

MARGARET (apologetically): I do love them — but it's not good for anyone to be together twenty-four hours a day.

CASH: Very well. Off you go. Try to find yourself a job. I'll be waiting here when you return.

(MARGARET turns to go, but turns back crestfallen.)

MARGARET: Where do you think I should go?

CASH: I suggest the Employment Exchange; and whilst you're out, try to get your children into a nursery.

(MARGARET goes. A CLERK from the Employment Exchange enters.)

CASH: Not much for you this morning, with male unemployment so high, but we'll try to keep the ladies happy with this little lot. (He hands the CLERK some cards.)

CLERK: Next!

(MARGARET comes in.)

CLERK: Name?

MARGARET: Mrs Johnson.

CLERK: Age?

MARGARET: 24.

CLERK: Previous experience.

MARGARET: Well, for the last few years I've been at home with my two children. Before that I was a filing clerk at a Mail Order firm. I could get good references from them.

CLERK: Well, here's one. They want a woman in a telephone sales and installation firm: hours, 40 a week; wages £16-£18. A clerk/typist.

MARGARET: I can't type.

CLERK: I see. That narrows the choice down considerably. Ah, here. Cashier at a Supermarket. Hours 43. Wages £15.42p. You work eight until five-thirty except Mondays and Fridays when you work till eight. Wednesday off: work Saturdays.

MARGARET: I'm afraid I don't want to work Saturdays, and I certainly can't work until eight at night.

CLERK: Well how about this one? It seems to be more in your line. Shop assistant on a meat counter: 44 hours a week, 28p an hour.

MARGARET: How much is that a week?

CLERK: Let's see. £12.30p.

MARGARET: That's not very much.

CLERK: Well, the opportunities for unqualified married women are very limited you know. Would you like an interview for this shop assistant's job?

MARGARET: Can I tell you later? I've got to try to get the children into a nursery.

CLERK: Well Mrs Johnson, I can't guarantee to hold it open for you. If someone comes in . . .

MARGARET: Yes I understand. I'll go right away.

(The CLERK goes. The NURSERY WOMAN enters.)

NURSERY WOMAN: Good afternoon, can I help you?

MARGARET: Yes, I'm just about to start a job and I was wondering if I could leave my children here during the day. I've got twins; they're four.

NURSERY WOMAN: Yes, we do have a few vacancies.

MARGARET: Oh good.

NURSERY WOMAN: Before I tell you how much it will cost . . .

MARGARET: But I thought it was free.

NURSERY WOMAN: Oh no. You're thinking of nursery schools for
pre-school education. Unfortunately there are very few of them, and
one has to register at least a year in advance. Here we look after the
children during the day but we don't offer a formal education.

MARGARET: I see, so how much does it cost?

NURSERY WOMAN: That depends on your gross earnings. How much
does your husband earn?

MARGARET: £22 per week.

NURSERY WOMAN: And how much will you be earning?

MARGARET: Just over £12.

NURSERY WOMAN: So that's £34 . . . Yes, it will be 99 pence per day
for the first child and 50 pence per day for the second.

MARGARET: But that's over £7.50 a week.

NURSERY WOMAN: That does include a breakfast, hot dinner, hot tea,
vitamins and hot drinks during the day, and a monthly medical
inspection with a doctor present. (She goes.)

MARGARET: Oh I see.

CASH: How much were the wages?

MARGARET: Just over £12.

CASH: And how much would it cost to put the children in a nursery?

MARGARET: Nearly £7.50.

CASH: Add another £1 for tax. How much is that?

MARGARET: £8.50.

CASH: Plus £1.50 for convenience foods — tinned, frozen — that's £10.
And a modest 50p for fares: that's £10.50. How much does that
leave from your wage of £12?

MARGARET: It's just not worth it! What is the point of going out to
work if there's nothing in your pocket at the end of the week?

CASH: There *is* no point, Sweetie. Look, I didn't want to disillusion
you — I thought it would be better for you to find out for yourself
— but I could have told you this would happen.

MARGARET: Well, it's not fair!

CASH: Margaret, with all the men out of work would it be fair for the
ladies to take the jobs?

MARGARET: What about the single women and the widows? There's nothing for them but the boring, badly-paid jobs.

CASH: Well just be thankful that you're not one of them! Now, Sweetie, let's see what my book has to say about it shall we? Ah yes . . .

(CASH begins to sing, while MARGARET holds the book.)

Men should fix things with hammers and saws,
Put up some shelves and paint the doors,
Go out to work and earn their keep,
Take the wife out once a week.

MARGARET: What can I do to get a job and earn a bit of money?

CASH: We're the breadwinners; you keep house; you must learn your place.

(He sings again, pointing to the book.)

Women should shop and cook the food,
Help their men and never be rude,
Be good mothers and care for the home,
Never find cause to moan.

(Before end of song MARGARET dispiritedly hands him the book and goes. CASH finishes the song with great panache, but looks rather foolish when he realises she has gone.

MARGARET's FATHER comes in.)

MARGARET (calling from off-stage): Hello Dad!

FATHER: Hello, love.

MARGARET: Bob said he'd put the kids to bed for me so I'll be all right for a while.

FATHER: How is Bob?

MARGARET: Oh, he's fine.

FATHER: And the kids?

MARGARET: They're all right. At least they're at school most of the day, so things are quite restful. How are things here?

FATHER: Not so good. Our Angela's really getting on my nerves.

MARGARET: It's her age.

FATHER: She's only 17 after all. Do you know what she's doing? She's off gallivanting with blokes with their hair down to their ankles. She's out till all hours of the night, and the other evening I was sat watching the Prime Minister on television and she starts shouting at him, saying he was running the country wrong — well if this is what being in the sixth form means I wish she'd left like you did. I mean she could be on drugs or anything.

MARGARET: Dad, don't believe anything you read in the papers. Our Angela's got a sensible head on her shoulders.

FATHER: Well I wish you'd have a word with her; I mean she won't listen to me.

(ANGELA comes in.)

ANGELA: Dad! What have you done with my papers? I laid them out especially and now they're scattered all over the place.

FATHER: This is how she talks to me! Look, don't you come telling me how to run my house.

ANGELA: If I've told you once, I've told you a thousand times! Leave my things alone.

FATHER: I'm going out before I lose my temper. (He goes.)

ANGELA: Stupid old fool.

MARGARET: You don't need to talk to him like that.

ANGELA: He's so stupid.

MARGARET: He may not be as well educated as you but he's only trying to help you.

ANGELA: Help me? You're joking.

MARGARET: Course he is, we're all trying to help you.

ANGELA: Do you mean that?

MARGARET: Yes.

ANGELA: All right . . . How do you get on the pill?

MARGARET: What!

ANGELA: How do you get on the pill?

MARGARET: What do you want with going on the pill?

ANGELA: I'm going out with this feller . . .

MARGARET: What do you want with going on the pill? I told your father you had a sensible head on your shoulders, but I was wrong.

ANGELA: I'm going out with this feller and we want to sleep together . . . In fact we have slept together. I don't want to get pregnant, so I want to know about contraception.

MARGARET: You're not pregnant, are you?

ANGELA: No I'm not pregnant. That's what I'm saying, I want to prevent that.

MARGARET: This schooling — where's it getting you? A factory girl could tell you that you don't do things like that otherwise you'll . . .

ANGELA: I *am* doing things like that.

MARGARET: Well you shouldn't — it's wrong.

ANGELA: Whether it's right or wrong I am doing it. I'm going to continue doing it, but I don't want to have a baby.

MARGARET: If you love him get married.

ANGELA: How can I? He's going to college soon, and anyway I don't want to marry him.

MARGARET: He's a student is he? He'll leave you in the lurch. It's all right for him; it'll be you who'll suffer. It's always the woman who suffers.

ANGELA: It's because I don't want to suffer that I want to take precautions. And all this about leaving me in the lurch, it's ridiculous. I want to sleep with him as much as he does with me.

MARGARET: Father's right, that's all I can say. They should have been stricter with you.

ANGELA: Look, forget all that. All I want is a bit of help. I can't go to Dr Morris, can I?

MARGARET: You cannot. He'd go straight to me Dad and quite right too.

ANGELA: What about these clinics? They can tell you whether you should have the pill or the cap or what.

MARGARET: What are you asking me for? You seem to know all about it anyway.

ANGELA: What do you and Bob use?

MARGARET: Well . . . that's always been Bob's responsibility.

ANGELA: So you use Durex.

MARGARET: Angela! I don't know what to say, I really don't.

ANGELA: I'm just asking you to help me. Can you help me or not? (Pause.) You can't can you?

MARGARET: It's not that I can't — I won't.

ANGELA: Thanks very much Margaret. You've been a lot of help! (She goes.)

CASH: Sweetie, let me congratulate you on the way you handled a very tricky situation.

MARGARET: I'm not sure I did the right thing.

CASH: Of course you did the right thing. She may be a little upset at the moment, but, mark my words, she'll come to thank you for your good advice later.

MARGARET: She won't thank me if she gets pregnant, will she?

CASH: She'll have to learn: if she wants babies, she'll have to get married. Now, Sweetie, I want to tell you about a council meeting which took place in our town, where very important people were discussing this very same problem.

(MARGARET goes.)

CASH (as Councillor): Ladies and gentlemen, one of the most disturbing proposals to come before this council for a long time is the proposal by the Health Committee that the services, supplies and advice given by the Family Planning Association should be provided free. Now I've no doubt that this will give rise to arguments about the moral rights or wrongs of the case but me, I'm a simple and straightforward sort of a man, and I'm worried about the financial side. I have some figures here from the Chief Medical Officer. They state quite clearly that if this service had been in operation last year it would have cost Bolton £8,500. Now that is bad enough, ladies and gentlemen: £8,500 that comes out of the ratepayers' pockets, but imagine what would happen when news of this free service gets around. The cost to the Bolton ratepayer would soar sky-high. To parents, I'd like to say this: would you like to think that your daughter, possibly your teen-age daughter, is going away for a dirty weekend and you are footing the bill? No. And to the young ladies I say this — My Dears, you have a safe and perfectly free form of contraceptive already at your disposal: you can say 'NO'.

COUNCILLOR BROUGHTON (a woman): Hear, hear!

COUNCILLOR WILLIAMS (a man): Listening to Councillor Cash, I hardly find it surprising that we, the authorities, are regarded with suspicion and hostility by a large number of young people when we display such a basic misunderstanding of their needs and stubbornly refuse to acknowledge any other view of sexual morality but our own. Like it or not, fellow councillors, ours is no longer a society which regards procreation as the only proper end of sexual intercourse. Let's not close our eyes to this truth.

　　Councillor Cash warns us of the cost to the taxpayer of introducing a free contraceptive service. All right — let's look at the cost of refusing to institute this service. The 150,000 unwanted children born annually in this country cost the taxpayer a total of £300 million in supplementary benefits, child-care and so on. Compare this with a figure of £35 million, the cost of providing a free service for every woman of child-bearing age. This is a fact: every pound spent on family planning would result in a saving for the Authority of anything up to one hundred pounds.

It is no use telling young people not to have sex — they'll decide that for themselves. In that case are we simply going to point stern fingers and accuse them of irresponsibility? In my own opinion, if young people use the facilities made available to them to prevent unwanted births — as has been the case in other parts of the country — then they *are* acting responsibly. It is our job, in this Council to show an equal sense of responsibility.

COUNCILLOR BROUGHTON: Ladies and gentlemen, I must reject this proposal. I reject it because it is a blatant attack on the moral standards of our young people. We are saying: 'Yes, go ahead and experiment with sex before marriage. It's all right as long as you don't get caught'. Have you thought of the terrifying implications of this? What is to prevent young girls who are given the pill from handing them around willy-nilly to their friends? What is to prevent them from becoming a generation of sterile women? What is to prevent disease from running rife in our town? I am not afraid, ladies and gentlemen, I am not afraid to stand in this Council Chamber tonight and declare myself a Christian. And I know that I stand with the vast majority of decent Bolton citizens; they would reject this as they would reject pornography, violence and drugs. I do not wish to let these people down. I wish to do the job for which I was elected namely to safeguard the well-being of this town.

CASH: You're so right, Councillor Broughton. Thank goodness we haven't all lost our moral values. The evening went well, I think.

COUNCILLOR BROUGHTON: I think so, Councillor Cash.

(COUNCILLORS BROUGHTON and WILLIAMS leave. MARGARET comes in, pulling on her overall.)

MARGARET: Mr Cash, I've got a job!

CASH: Now calm down, Margaret. If you have something to say we'd all like to hear it. Now, you've got a job?

MARGARET: In a factory.

CASH: And what about the children?

MARGARET: They're at school most of the day now, and Carol, next door, says they can go into her house for the last hour before I get home.

CASH: Margaret, if you are determined to take this job I have a very important story to read to you. (They sit.) Listen very carefully. 'The Fable of the Greedy Blackbird.'

(During the story MARGARET becomes bored and fidgety.)

'Once upon a time, there were two blackbirds, Mr Blackbird and Mrs Blackbird, and they lived in a lovely nest. One happy day two baby blackbirds were born. Mr Blackbird went out hunting and Mrs Blackbird stayed at home and looked after the nest. But one day Mrs Blackbird became greedy, and she wandered off looking for the trees with the biggest berries, and she neglected her nest. One day she came home to find that Mr Blackbird had gone — he had flown away with the pretty little blackbird from the next nest . . . '

MARGARET: That's a silly story!

CASH: Margaret!!

MARGARET: Bob isn't like that. (She turns to go. Then, rather patronisingly:) Thank you for the story, Mr Cash.

CASH (to audience): Such a shame another baby hasn't come along: that's what she really needs.

MARGARET: I'm over here, Florrie.

FLORRIE (entering with flask and mugs): I needed this, didn't you?

WORKMAN (coming in): Hello, ladies. Are you coming tonight?

MARGARET: What's this?

WORKMAN: Union meeting about the men's pay rise.

MARGARET: I can't, I've got to get home to my husband.

WORKMAN: What's the matter, can't he wait until bedtime?

FLORRIE: She means 'the tea'! We've got two jobs, you know. Listen, you'd get more women coming to union meetings if you thought about them for a change.

WORKMAN: What do you mean, love, they're never off my mind!

FLORRIE: You know what I mean.

WORKMAN: Oh, all this equal pay rubbish.

FLORRIE: It's not rubbish. We work hard, don't we?

WORKMAN: Yes, lovey.

FLORRIE: We work eight to five, don't we?

WORKMAN: Yes, lovey.

FLORRIE: Then what we want is equal pay for equal work.

WORKMAN: Yes, lovey.

FLORRIE: Well then.

WORKMAN: Well then, all you've got to do is throw a couple of hundred weight of steel on those rollers, drive a forklift truck round the yard in the rain, chop a couple of fingers off on the lathe, then start asking for equal pay for equal work.

FLORRIE: Oh, you think you're so clever, don't you?

MARGARET: No, he's right, Florrie. I couldn't do anything like that.

FLORRIE: Nobody's asking you to, love. He knows what I'm on about — we do our job; they do theirs. I'd like to see them on our bench.

WORKMAN: Heaven forbid. See me doing women's work.

FLORRIE: Yes, heaven forbid! We don't think so much of it either, but what I'm saying is, we do it, we work hard, and I for one am sick of being the poor relation.

MARGARET (joking): You should become a shop steward, Florrie!

FLORRIE: That's a good idea, love. I might do just that.

WORKMAN: Yes, the Pakis have got theirs — old what's-it — Patel. Why don't you go the whole hog? Join Women's Lib. Burn your bra!

(MARGARET laughs.)

FLORRIE (to WORKMAN): Oh, shut it you!

WORKMAN: Anyway, are you coming tonight?

FLORRIE: I've told you, I'll be there. (WORKMAN goes out.) What about you, Margaret?

MARGARET: All right, I'll come too.

FLORRIE: What about the tea?

MARGARET: Well, Bob's a strong union man himself, he'll understand.

(They go.)

BOB (at home, wondering where his wife is): Margaret? . . . MARGARET! (He hears a knock at the door.) Ah, at last. (He opens the door.) Oh!

MR CROSS (stepping in): Good evening. Mr Johnson is it? Is Mrs Johnson in?

BOB: No she isn't. Can I help you?

MR CROSS: Well, my name is Mr Cross. I'm from the Tenants' Association. I called a few days ago and spoke to your wife. She probably told you.

BOB: No she didn't.

MR CROSS: Well the Tenants' Association is fighting the Fair Rents Act, and Mrs Johnson signed our petition saying that she won't pay the £1 increase in rent next month. She said she would collect some more signatures from people round here, so I've brought her some petition forms — if you could give them to her . . . (He turns to go.) Oh and Mr Johnson . . . We'd be very glad if you would sign it yourself! Every little helps, you know.

BOB: You'll not get my signature on this, mate. We'll be paying the increase in this house.

MR CROSS: So you're happy to pay the £1 are you? And the 50p next April, and the 50p next October?

BOB: If we don't pay it, they'll just evict us. I'm not having my family out on the streets.

MR CROSS: We've got over 4,000 signatures on this petition already, Mr Johnson; and people will refuse to pay the increase all over the country. They can't throw us all out. Look, the Government is going to make 250 million clear profit out of us in the first year of this Bill, a huge profit for them and a wage cut for us — a rent rise amounts to a wage cut, Mr Johnson. You wouldn't stand for that at work, would you?

BOB: That's different. We've got the union to back us up there. If you think you and a handful of housewives are going to beat this Government, you're daft. And don't come back here getting my wife involved in all this rubbish. (He slams the door as CROSS leaves, and sits down again.)

MARGARET (running in): I'm sorry I'm late, love. I've been to a union meeting. But I've got a nice piece of liver; it shouldn't take long . . .

BOB: I haven't time to wait, Margaret. You know I had to go out early tonight. Get me some beans on toast.

MARGARET: You should have heard Florrie in the meeting. She was great. She said women should get the same pay as men and that if they didn't start listening to our demands we wouldn't come to union meetings anymore.

BOB: They'd be better off without her, anyway.

MARGARET: Well, I don't know, Bob. A woman's wage is necessary these days. I mean, I need to go out to work, don't I? If I didn't, we wouldn't have been able to have a new stair-carpet, we wouldn't have had a holiday for years . . .

BOB: You'll be telling me next that I should stay at home and you should be the breadwinner. I'd like to see us manage on £15 a week.

MARGARET: Well in 1974 women will have to get the same pay as men because it's the law. (She goes out to the kitchen.)

BOB: It's 1975 and you know what will happen then? Women just won't be employed, they'll be too expensive.

MARGARET (off): Oh, I'm too tired to argue with you now.

BOB (picking up the petition forms): But you won't be too tired to go traipsing round the estate encouraging people to break the law, will you?

MARGARET (off): What's that, love?

BOB: Your boyfriend from the Tenants' Association has been round. He left these for you.

MARGARET (coming back in and taking the forms): Mr Cross! Oh I'm sorry I missed him — four sheets, thirty a sheet. I think I'll start tomorrow . . .

BOB: You won't start at all! This fellow, Cross, must have turned your head. And you had no right to sign that petition. If I say we're going to pay the increase, we'll pay it.

MARGARET: But Bob, you know it's not right! Unless we put up a fight now, we'll be paying double rent. You don't agree with the Government making a profit out of council houses, do you. They'll be just like private rents — you've often said yourself they're scandalous. Look at our Angela, paying £6 a week for a flat with an outside lavatory.

BOB: But we have to pay a fair rent. Now look, Margaret, let me explain, people in council houses are subsidised at the moment, and . . .

MARGARET: But so are people buying their own houses! They get twice as much subsidy as we do in tax relief. Mr Cross says . . .

BOB: Oh Mr Cross, Mr Cross! You should've married Mr Cross if you think so much of him. But whilst I'm your husband you will not go round this estate showing yourself up! (He takes the forms.)

MARGARET (snatching them back): I will go! What right have you to stop me? You're not my jailor! (She goes.)

BOB: You're a fine one to take on the Government — you can't even get tea for me and the kids.

CASH: Good man, Bob!

BOB: What can you do with them?

CASH: She's enjoying testing her strength against yours, Bob, but what she really wants is for you to come along and show her who's master. They're funny creatures, women. But what would we do without them? Seriously, Bob, you were right to put your foot down. You realise what is at stake here: your wife is in danger; she's going to make a fool of herself in front of the neighbours; she's already neglecting the house, and she's getting herself involved with some pretty dangerous people — this Cross for example.

BOB: He's probably a bloody Commie.

CASH: Indeed, Bob. But he's also a very clever man. He realises that we men have a firm grasp of political reality, so he is taking his subversive activities into the heart of the family. He is corrupting our wives, Bob. Well, it's the same old story, petitions, meetings, anti-social

gatherings, demonstrations, arrests, and — inevitably — prison.
(BOB gets up to follow MARGARET.) But there is no need for you to
worry, Bob. Fortunately Margaret is merely infatuated with this chap
Cross. Why not take her mind off it. Look I've got a couple of tickets
here for a television show; why not take her along and give her a good
time.

BOB: Thank you Mr Cash. And thank you for your advice. (He goes.)

('Up, up and away' music. Enter CASH, as the compere of a T.V. show.)

CASH: Yes, up, up and away indeed, ladies and gentlemen, for now the
time has come for our lucky contestants to follow their fortunes
towards that second honeymoon in the Costa del Sol. It's time once
again for the 'Mr and Mrs Game'. (Applause.) And speaking of Mr and
Mrs, ladies and gentlemen, take my wife . . . please! (CASH laughs.)
I'm not saying that she's fat, ladies and gentlemen, just that when I
carried her across the threshold I had to make three journeys. (Laughs.)
It's true. But seriously, I was talking to the vicar after the ceremony,
and I asked him how much I owed him and he said, 'There's no set
fee, my son, however if you would like to make a contribution'. So I
slipped him ten bob — (Laughs.) — he took one look at the wife and
gave me seven and six change. (Laughs.) Ah, but I'm not complaining
ladies and gentlemen, why only the other day I got a new car for the
wife . . . not a bad exchange I thought. (Laughs.) Well, less of the
frivolities ladies and gentlemen, and on with the show, and what a
showing she is . . . Every married man's friend, the sexy, scintillating
Samantha.

(Applause. Enter SAMANTHA.)

Samantha, ladies and gentlemen, the girl with the two large . . . an opinion
of herself. (CASH laughs.) Thank you, Sam. A lovely girl, Samantha,
not much up here, but plenty where it counts. (Laughs.) But seriously,
ladies and gentlemen, the time has come for you to meet the first
two contestants who want to play 'The Mr and Mrs Game'.

(Applause as SAMANTHA brings on BOB and MARGARET.)

And they are —

SAMANTHA: Mr and Mrs Bob Johnson, from Bolton, Lancashire.

(Applause.)

CASH: Hello, Bob. (He shakes BOB's hand.) How are you? And tell me
what do you do for a living?

BOB (quietly): I'm a maintenance electrician.

CASH: A little louder, please, Bob, so we can all hear.

BOB: I'm a maintenance electrician.

CASH: An electrician, Bob. Bit of a bright spark are you. (CASH laughs.) Give the wife a few shocks, do you. (He laughs and turns to MARGARET.) Hello, my love, and tell me what's your name?

MARGARET: Margaret.

CASH: Mrs Bob Johnson, ladies and gentlemen. Isn't she a sweetie? Now, Samantha, if you would place Bob in his chair . . . Bob you go with Samantha, that's it, sit there, Bob. (SAMANTHA sits on BOB's knee.) Now, now, Bob, put her down, we don't know where she's been. (CASH laughs.) Now my love, if you'd like to sit down here. (He places MARGARET in a chair.) That's it. And for the benefit of those people who do not know how to play our little game, I will quickly explain the rules. I am going to ask Bob a series of questions, and he is going to give me the answers. I am then going to ask the same questions of Mrs Bob Johnson, and if she gives me the same answers, they win a prize. Simple, ladies and gentlemen, but there is a catch, isn't there always. (CASH laughs.) Mrs Bob Johnson will be forced to tell the real truth, because, throughout the entire proceedings, Mrs Bob Johnson will be hypnotised.

(Applause. SAMANTHA hands CASH a shiny medallion.)

And now, ladies and gentlemen, I am going to attempt to hypnotise Mrs Bob Johnson. Now I want you to relax, my love, that's it, sit nice and comfortably, I want you to concentrate on this, my love. You are feeling sleepy, very sleepy, your eyes are getting heavier, your mind is slipping away, slipping away, slipping away. Ladies and gentlemen, Mrs Bob Johnson is now hypnotised.

(Applause. SAMANTHA takes the medallion from CASH.)

However, ladies and gentlemen, though Mrs Bob Johnson is in this state of deep hypnosis, she can, in fact, hear everything that I say, is that true my love?

MARGARET: Yes, Mr Cash.

CASH: Fine. However, when I click my fingers you will be able to hear nothing at all. (He clicks his fingers.) Can you hear me, my love? (Silence.) Fine, fine. Ladies and gentlemen, Mrs Bob Johnson can now hear nothing at all, so we are safe to start the questioning. And so straight on, Bob, the first question is this. (He takes some cards out of his pocket.) 'What is your good lady wife's favourite colour?' Now there's plenty of time, Bob. And remember, Mrs Johnson is forced to tell the real truth. 'What is your wife's favourite colour?'

BOB: Blue.

CASH: And Bob plumps for blue without any hesitation. (Applause. CASH goes over to MARGARET.) Let's see what Mrs Johnson has to say. (He clicks his fingers.) Would you tell me, my love, for ten points, what is your favourite colour?

MARGARET: Blue.

CASH: And that's ten points for Mr and Mrs Bob Johnson. (Applause. CASH clicks his fingers and moves over to BOB.) Now for ten more points, Bob, can you tell me, please, 'What has been the happiest moment for Mrs Johnson in the last two years?'

BOB: When I bought her an eternity ring.

CASH: You're quite sure, Bob?

BOB: Yes.

CASH: A loving present from a thoughtful husband, ladies and gentlemen. (Applause. CASH moves over to MARGARET and clicks his fingers.) My love, will you tell me please, what has been the happiest moment for you in the last two years?

MARGARET: When I got my first wage packet from the factory. I went straight out and bought a lovely purple jumper.

CASH: That is not the right answer. (He clicks his fingers and moves over to BOB.) Now, time's getting on, Bob. Let us see if we can increase your score. 'Is there anything at all that you simply do not understand about your wife?' Plenty of time, Bob, plenty of time.

BOB: I don't understand why she always gives me sausages – she knows I don't like them.

CASH: Food for thought there, Bob. (Applause. CASH moves over to MARGARET and clicks his fingers.) Now my love, for ten vital points, would you tell me please, do you think there is anything that Bob does not understand about you?

MARGARET: He doesn't understand that there are times when I want to make love. He thinks he's the only one who can feel sexy, but . . .

CASH (hurriedly): That is not the right answer. (He clicks his fingers. MARGARET wakes out of her trance.) And that, ladies and gentlemen, is all we have time for today.

(SAMANTHA ushers off MARGARET and BOB. Applause.)

MARGARET: Did we win, Bob?

CASH: Well, that's it. Don't forget to be with us next week when, who knows, the lucky Mr and Mrs could be you.

(Enter SAMANTHA.)

CASH: So for this week, ladies and gentlemen, from Samantha it's . . .

SAMANTHA: Goodnight.

CASH: And from me — Goodnight and God bless. (They go.)

MARGARET: Bob.

BOB: Yes. What love?

MARGARET: I'm pregnant again. (Pause.) Well — I'm pregnant again.

BOB: What am I supposed to say? . . . It's not what we wanted but . . .

MARGARET: But what?

BOB: We'll . . . just have to start knitting that's all.

MARGARET: And I'd have to give up my job, spend five years looking after it, washing nappies, getting up in the middle of the night.

BOB: You did for the twins.

MARGARET: I know I did and I enjoyed it, most of the time — but I don't want to go through all that again. I'm happy with the four of us — another would wreck all that. We'd have to scrimp and save — I'd have to stay at home all day. No, Bob.

BOB: No what? It's a fact. It's done and we'll just have to put up with it.

MARGARET: I'm not going to put up with it.

BOB: What do you mean?

MARGARET: I don't have to put up with it. I want an abortion.

BOB: Who gave you that idea?

MARGARET: Bob, I've got a mind of my own. I decided. Neither of us wanted another child — we shouldn't have to have it. It should be up to us.

BOB: That's all changed now.

MARGARET: How's it changed?

BOB: No, love.

MARGARET: Look, it's not the way I would have wanted it, but I can't go back to all that Bob. I can't. I'm going to see Dr Morris tomorrow. I'll tell him I don't want it — and he may be able to get me an abortion. It's legal now. Well, Bob?

BOB: What's it got to do with me? You seem to have decided already.

MARGARET: I want you to agree. I feel it's the best for both of us — for all of us — you see that, don't you? (Pause.) O.K. What do you suggest I do?

BOB: You do what you like — I'm going out. (He goes.)

(The G.P. enters.)

G.P.: Well Mrs Johnson — as your G.P. I must say that I don't think an abortion is necessary. According to the law an abortion is allowed if a continued pregnancy would endanger a woman's life or harm her physical or mental condition — or that of her baby — to a greater extent than if the foetus were aborted. I have examined you, and I find you perfectly sound in both mind and body.

MARGARET: But I don't want the baby, Doctor.

G.P.: Mrs Johnson, are you mentally or physically ill?

MARGARET: No, but . . .

G.P.: Then I'm unable to recommend you for an abortion. My dear, I know this baby wasn't expected, and at the moment you are depressed. But there must have been times during your first pregnancy when you wished you were slim and pretty again. Margaret, think of it this way, if you were to have this child aborted, it would be like killing Tommy or Jane. I suggest that, if you are still depressed in a week or two, you make an appointment to see me again. Good day, Mrs Johnson. (He goes.)

(CAROL comes in.)

CAROL: Well love, I don't think I can help you, but I do know how you feel; I'd go crazy if I got caught again, but what can you do?

MARGARET: Well, abortion's legal now — lots of people have it done.

CAROL: But you've got to know the right people love — doctors and specialists. Look, a girl I used to work with went to one of these back street places. I don't know exactly what was done — hot baths and knitting needles or something — but I do know she bled for days, and they had to rush her to hospital in the end. You're not going to try one of those?

MARGARET: Look, I'm not going to a back street place, but it's different with doctors. They say it's safer than having a baby — but where can I go now Dr Morris said 'no'?

CAROL: That's what I say — you've got to know the right people. You could write up to the problems page in *Woman*, they might tell you. Though come to think of it, I don't remember reading anything about abortions there, unless it's one of those where you have to send a stamped, addressed envelope and call yourself 'Distressed of Davenport'.

MARGARET: I'm 'Bewildered of Bolton'.

CAROL: You are, aren't you love? Margaret, you could write to one of those pregnancy testing places . . .

MARGARET: But I know I'm pregnant . . .

CAROL: Yes, but they might be able to give you an address. It's worth a try, love. (She goes.)

(The RECEPTIONIST enters.)

MARGARET: Excuse me.

RECEPTIONIST: Good afternoon. Can I help you?

MARGARET: Yes, I was waiting to see the doctor about an abor . . .

RECEPTIONIST (curtly): What is your name, please?

MARGARET: Mrs Johnson.

RECEPTIONIST: What time is your appointment, Mrs Johnson?

MARGARET: I haven't got one, yet.

RECEPTIONIST: I see. You've come to make one. Which doctor did you want to see?

MARGARET: I don't know. Is there more than one?

RECEPTIONIST: Let's have a look at Mr Lester's appointments then, shall we? How about a week on Friday at 3pm?

MARGARET: I was hoping to see him this afternoon.

RECEPTIONIST: I'm afraid that's quite out of the question.

MARGARET: But it's urgent.

RECEPTIONIST: Yes, well all I can suggest is that you take a seat and we'll see if there's a cancellation.

MARGARET: Yes. Will he be able . . .

RECEPTIONIST: If you'd like to take a seat, Mrs Johnson.

MARGARET: Thank you.

(Pause.)

MARGARET: Can you tell me how much it will be?

RECEPTIONIST: Yes indeed. £10 . . .

MARGARET: Ten!?

RECEPTIONIST: . . . For this appointment. Any further consultations will be included in the overall charge.

MARGARET: What about the abortion?

RECEPTIONIST: Doctor will give you details about any treatment he advises, Mrs Johnson.

MARGARET: Yes, but how much will it be?

RECEPTIONIST: That depends entirely on the nature of your case — how many days you stay in the clinic, whether there are any complications, but the doctor knows best about that, doesn't he?

MARGARET: Look if it's . . .

RECEPTIONIST: Mrs Johnson, treatment is rarely more than two hundred pounds, even in the most difficult of cases. (The RECEPTIONIST goes.)

(Enter BOB.)

MARGARET: So I just had to crawl out. £150 at the minimum. And that's without the doctor's fees. She was so smug and satisfied — she'd hardly tell me a bloody thing.

BOB: What is it to her? She said they were busy. They're exploiting hundreds of poor buggers — they're raking it in at £150 a time. Look, it might be much simpler just to have it.

MARGARET: No. I've not finished yet. I saw Dr Morris again, and I really pestered him like Carol told me to. He's fixed me an appointment to see the gynaecologist at the hospital tomorrow afternoon.

BOB: Morris will have told him what he thinks. You don't stand a chance.

MARGARET: Well who does stand a chance? I've thought and thought about it. It's not some whim or fancy. I've decided that I don't want this baby. This gynaecologist can give me an abortion on the National Health and I won't have to pay a thing.

BOB: I wish we'd never got into this bloody mess in the first place.

MARGARET: *You* wish we'd never got into it! How do you think I feel? I'm sorry, love. It's not your fault. Look, will you come with me tomorrow, to the hospital?

BOB: What can I say?

MARGARET: You don't have to say anything. Just come with me — I'd feel better if you did.

BOB: All right — I'll take time off work. (He goes.)

(The GYNAECOLOGIST comes in, wiping his hands on a towel. MARGARET is doing up her skirt.)

GYNAECOLOGIST: Sit down. (He begins filling in a form.) Did you have regular periods before conception?

MARGARET: Yes.

GYNAECOLOGIST: Any abnormal discharge between periods before conception or any since?

MARGARET: No.

GYNAECOLOGIST: Do you have satisfactory sexual intercourse with your husband?

MARGARET: . . . Yes.

GYNAECOLOGIST: Any physical problems there?

MARGARET: No.

GYNAECOLOGIST: Is your husband the father of the child? Come on, Mrs Johnson, you are the only one who can answer that.

MARGARET: Yes.

GYNAECOLOGIST: Mrs Johnson — my job is to bring healthy babies into this world for healthy mothers.

MARGARET: But I don't want . . .

GYNAECOLOGIST: You are a strong healthy woman. I can find no grounds for terminating your pregnancy . . .

MARGARET: But don't you see that I've decided I want . . .

GYNAECOLOGIST: . . . Particularly at the expense of the State.

MARGARET: But Dr Morris sent me to you — he said you would be able to help.

GYNAECOLOGIST: Dr Morris is not a gynaecologist.

MARGARET: But you do abortions.

GYNAECOLOGIST: I terminate pregnancies only when it is absolutely necessary.

MARGARET: Well don't you even want to know why I want . . .

GYNAECOLOGIST: Mrs Johnson, I have no time to listen to the abnormal fantasies of a selfish woman.

MARGARET: Well, who do you suggest I go to now?

GYNAECOLOGIST: I suggest your husband. Now pull yourself together and prepare yourself for what to other women is a happy event. Good day. (He goes.)

(Enter BOB.)

BOB: What right had he to ask whose kid it was. Who the hell does he think he is?

MARGARET: He just wouldn't listen, Bob. I tried to explain, but he wouldn't listen. He tried to make me feel guilty — make out I was a murderer and there was something wrong with me.

BOB: Just put him out of your mind, love — he thinks he's bloody God.

MARGARET: But Dr Morris said he was the one to help me. I couldn't see another doctor like that again — he didn't care about what I said or felt. He said there were no reasons at all — but I can't have it . . . I can't.

BOB: No, love. Don't worry. Your Angela came round and left this address: The Merseyside Pregnancy Advisory Service.

MARGARET: What is it?

BOB: It's a clinic — it'll cost £60.

MARGARET: It's not back street is it?

BOB: No — that's the first thing I asked. It's run by doctors — it's so cheap because it's non-profit making. She told me it was good.

MARGARET: I'll go and see them. (They both go.)

(Pause. MARGARET and BOB come back.)

MARGARET: It's too late. They do them up to three months, and I'm nearly five.

BOB: That's definite is it?

MARGARET: There was one way they could have done it. They start you off in labour — it takes between eight and fifteen hours and then the baby's born — but it's dead.

BOB: You don't want that, do you love? (She shakes her head.) Did they treat you well?

MARGARET: The first people to treat me like a human being — if only I'd got there two months earlier . . . Look, I'd like to be on my own for a while, love. (BOB goes.)

CASH (coming forward): Sweetie — let me say how pleased I am things have turned out like this and, you mark my words, you'll be as pleased as I am when the happy day arrives. And look, I've a little present . . . there you are.

(MARGARET opens the wrapped parcel.)

MARGARET: Mumsie-care.

CASH: And Carol's got a surprise for you. Carol!

(CAROL comes in, holding out a case of baby clothes to MARGARET.)

CAROL: You're very welcome, love.

CASH: Put them on there, Carol. Now let's see what we've got, shall we? There, you said how pretty that was, didn't you? You take them all — you can sort them out later. Now isn't that kind of Carol?

CAROL (embarrassed): Anything I can do, love . . . (She goes.)

CASH: And Bob's got a surprise for you as well. Bob! Come in.

BOB (entering): We'll make the best of it, love.

CASH: Do you remember this, Sweetie? (CASH gets BOB to show MARGARET the smock he's brought in.) Remember how pretty you looked in that? Bob. You help her on with it. I'll take these, Sweetie. (He takes the clothes.) Come on, Bob. Pretty as a picture.

And now, Sweetie, we'll choose a name. You come with me and sit down there — (BOB goes.) — and we'll choose a name from my book. Let's see what we've got shall we. Sarah? Eliza . . . No? . . . I know: if it's a boy we'll call him Toby!

MARGARET (enraged): They're stupid names and that's a stupid book. It's all lies. (She seizes the book.) Right from the beginning it's been lies. Look at this first story . . .

CASH: Calm down, don't get yourself into a state, Sweetie Pie.

MARGARET (throwing the book to the floor): My name isn't Sweetie Pie — it's Margaret! (She goes.)

CASH (losing his temper): You come back here! (He remembers audience and composes himself as he picks up the book.) I apologise for her little outburst, ladies and gentlemen. But ladies in her condition are a little unpredictable, aren't they?! And now I'm sure you're longing to know how my little story ends . . . Well, I'll tell you. (He reads.) 'And in due course the princess gave birth to a bouncing baby boy — and they all lived happily ever after'.

And that, ladies and gentlemen, is the end of my story. I hope you've enjoyed it. And now it's time for us all to go. I have to take the good lady out to dinner and I'd better not be late had I? Good night. (He leaves.)

Octagon Theatre Bolton
Theatre in Education Company

WOMEN AS...

. . . SEX SYMBOLS

. . . SIMPLETONS

. . . MACHINES

... DOORMATS

This is a very remarkable doormat...
It wipes your feet!

THE OMEX MATADOR

... EGO PROPS

Jean Vermes, 'A Secretary's Guide to Dealing with People'.

'In a way, getting along with an executive is like getting along with a husband, only more so. You must adjust to his idiosyncracies and he to yours; but since he is your superior there is naturally more adjustment done on your part that on his.'

... AND PURITY ITSELF

That Femfresh Feeling
ake up to it with Femfresh vaginal deodorant

P.S.

They also double as automatic washers, cleaners & polishers, baby-minders, dish-washers, cooks, tea-makers, bed partners, and cheap labour.

NOTES ON AUDIENCE REACTION

Sweetie Pie was performed to sixth forms, fifth forms, Women's Institutes, Tenants' Associations, Colleges of Education, Arts Centres, Community Associations and to the general public in our own studio. We thought it was a successful piece of work, but the response varied enormously from audience to audience.

Fifth and Sixth Forms. There was a very strong sympathy with Margaret but we felt that some of the scenes were too far outside their own experience for them to identify closely. Equally, in schools, there was always a tense interest in the contraception scene between Margaret and Angela. It might have been better to have further developed the character of the younger sister: we were afraid that some sixth formers might presume that their academic ability would necessarily save them from the difficulties Margaret had to face. It would have been a better sixth form programme if more of the script had dealt with the socialisation of boys and girls that goes on from birth right through school, and if we had put more emphasis on job discrimination, the fashion rat-race and sexuality.

There was a good deal of naiveté about Cash's first speeches: the 'Sweetie and the Happy Event' story often didn't raise a titter — many of them really were as trusting as Margaret at this point. But at the end when he produces the baby clothes for the second time, the strength of their feeling against Cash was often shown in bitter mutters and occasional obscenities.

Despite the reservations we had, we felt from the audience response and from conversations after the show that it was a powerful theatrical experience for them; we hoped that, even if they didn't always draw general principles from the play, some of the characters would be memorable enough to contribute something to women's growing awareness of their situation.

Performances Outside School. We found that we had written a play which was more successful with older people than with sixth formers. The response varied enormously, but, in all the shows, the women in the audience were delighted to see the common concerns of their lives made the subject of a play. The first scene with the baby clothes and the housework scene were followed attentively — this was something most of the women had experienced; some audiences roared with laughter, others concentrated quietly for the most part, but the identification with Margaret was complete.

We thought that the contraception and abortion issues might cause offence in the Women's Institutes, but we had underestimated the

women in that organisation. Our first performance to a Women's Institute
audience was in a school hall, packed with women of all ages; they sat on
the window sills, the gym equipment and the prop tables, and it was one
of the most intense and enjoyable evenings of the entire run. We did
several lunch-time and evening performances in our studio (though the
play is too long to be a successful lunch-time entertainment), and I
remember one of them particularly: at the beginning of the show it
seemed to be a badly mixed audience — one side was composed of
working-class women most of whom were, or had been, on rent strike;
they didn't regard any of the first scenes as ironic, they took them straight,
and were puzzled and disturbed by the laughter from the other side of
the audience which was composed mainly of students and women
liberationists. But, as the show progressed, the audience grew together,
the concentration increased, the performance that night was excellent,
and, at the end, I felt that the play had achieved its most ambitious aim
— not merely to persuade people to identify and sympathise with
Margaret, but to convince them, however briefly, that the conditions of
her life can and must change.

NOTES ON STAGING *SWEETIE PIE*

We played in thrust, the audience on three sides of a rectangle; there
were four entrances at the corners of the rectangle and two from behind
the screen which formed the fourth side. Prop tables at the end of the
vomitories were in full view of the audience, and actors would collect
props and costume and walk quietly but openly to the position of their
next entrance.

We cast the play so that it could be performed by as few as three
actors and two actresses. One actor played Cash in all his manifestations,
another played Bob and the three suitors, and the third played all the
other male characters. Of the two actresses, one played Margaret and the
other took all the other female roles. But this is a minimum, and more
actors could of course be used.

There are many references to Bolton in the play and most characters
spoke with the local accent — the fact that Cash didn't was a telling
difference. It is essential that groups who use the script alter such details,
making them relevant to their own community and use the strengths of
local identity to put the message of the play across forcefully. Bad
northern accents are not only irrelevant to other communities, they are
downright insulting to the people of Bolton.

NOTES ON THE SCRIPTING OF *SWEETIE PIE*

It was very satisfying, in writing *Sweetie Pie*, to create a good woman's part. There are many more parts for men than women in theatre, and those actresses who are lucky enough to be employed, too often find themselves playing the boring stereotypes of sexy young girl, homely wife, or buxom whore. In turn these parts reinforce the traditional roles of women for the audiences who watch them − it is a vicious circle. The writing of plays like *Sweetie Pie* is one of a number of signs which indicate that the circle is beginning to be broken. The growing number of struggles for redefinition of women's role in society is slowly being reflected in the theatre. More women writers and directors and increasingly critical actresses will lead to more and better parts for women.

The Octagon Theatre-in-Education Company is run as a democracy: all members have responsibility for decisions about the group and the work. It is one of an increasing number of theatre groups who feel a need to control their own working conditions and, consequently, the material they perform. At the same time the traditionally distinct functions of writer, director, and actor are being questioned. There are new experiments involving combinations of roles or, at least, new lines of division. Our retrospective assessment of our experience in writing *Sweetie Pie* bears some relevance to those experiments.

We felt that *Sweetie Pie* was a good script; we had all contributed to it and were anxious that it should succeed in performance, but, despite several changes and additions during the run, there were still many parts that we didn't like. Our ambitious concept of Mr Cash's part, for instance, was never fully realised. We felt, too, that bits of the script were woolly and lacking in theatrical precision. There are undoubted advantages in being both actor and writer, but one of the limitations is the difficulty of looking at the script objectively; various members of the cast have different opinions about what is most effective − it is sometimes difficult to decide who makes the final choice. Relationships between director and actors are inevitably complex, not only because there is no finished script to refer to, but because, as co-authors of the script, the actors feel they have a right to influence the interpretation. During a good session there need be no friction: actors, director and material stimulate and complement each other and there is a unanimous feeling of progress. But there are difficult rehearsals in which no progress is made, the first performance looms, and there is a need for one individual to finish the script and present it to the actors so that they can rehearse it as they would a traditional script. To help meet this need the Octagon Theatre-in-Education team contracted a writer to begin work with them in July 1974. He will not work in isolation from the group and, no doubt, his presence will bring additional complications, but it is hoped that with his special skills, he will be able to shape and improve scenes which prove intractable during improvisation and will bring a unifying influence to the script as a whole.

If you would like regular information on new Methuen plays and theatre books, please write to
The Marketing Department
Eyre Methuen Ltd
North Way
Andover
Hants